EWES AND I

EWES AND I

Elizabeth Arthursson

with illustrations by Steven Binks

SOUVENIR PRESS

ISBN 0 285 62835 6

Photoset by Rowland Phototypesetting Ltd
Bury St Edmunds, Suffolk

Printed in Great Britain by
Mackays of Chatham Ltd

For Sally, Tim and Miles,
James and Donna,
with love and happy memories
of summer in the country

Chapter One

It all started one summer, so simply, when we bought a small Tudor farmhouse in the middle of nowhere. It was a long, hot summer—a summer of roses and strawberry wine. Pale chalk hill blue butterflies and tawny speckled skippers danced over daisy-strewn meadows, over clover and lucerne. Fat bumble bees drifted across the lawn and every night we heard the nightingales singing in a thicket two fields away. The air was warm and scented. On a day when the distant hills danced with heat and the wheat was a tall, rippling, grey-green sea, I found our little farmhouse in the fields.

Gerald and I and our two children, Katy, then fourteen, and Tom, eleven, had been living for three years in the centre of a village in north Essex. It was a pretty little place. The houses clustered on a hill around the church and below it was the river valley—beautiful in spring with the pale fields and the dark, catkined alders leaning beside the river banks. The village had a green covered in huge old lime trees. Every spring their new leaves were smooth and shining, and when the fragrant flowers appeared the humming of bees swarming over them could be heard all along the main village street. There was a wonderful baker's shop that baked its own bread; I used to walk up the hill in the early mornings and carry home the still-hot loaves, nibbling pieces from their ends as I walked. The rest of the family always laughed at the state of their bread by the time I arrived back.

Our house, dating back to 1442, was one of the oldest in the village and exceedingly beautiful. I loved it for its age—its mellow beams, its lichen-covered roof, its lattice windows and gutters full of dozy sparrows. I adore old houses: they have a charm, a spell about them, and as soon as I stepped into this house I had been captivated by it. It had ancient doors and winding staircases, secret passages and inglenook fireplaces. In summer I filled them with bowls of delphiniums and lilies and poppies, and sat there looking up the chimney to the square of blue sky at the top, where I could see the swallows flying. In winter we roasted chestnuts by enormous log fires and watched the spiral of smoke drifting up to the stars. The house was perfect and the garden reasonably large. I planted vines and apple trees, and a large medieval-style herb garden between old red bricks on the terrace at the back. I used to sit in the herb garden with my spinning wheel, spinning up fleeces which I got from my farmer friend, Ian, who lived about three miles away. He had 200 ewes, and I used to go and watch the shearing every summer.

That summer I went as usual, one hot June afternoon. Ian came out of the farmhouse as I arrived, dressed in his customary corduroy trousers and wellingtons, a smile lighting up his blue eyes. When he smiled I always felt a slight uneasiness, an urge to take that step too near, instead of keeping the distance that friends and acquaintances maintain between each other. Only lovers cross that imaginary line, that unseen barrier that we all keep around us. When Ian smiled like that I always wanted to put out my hand to touch his arm, to feel his warm body under the checked shirt.

'Hello, Lizzy, I'm just mixing up some milk for the orphans. Do you want to come and feed one?'

'Yes, please,' I said, following him into the kitchen.

The moment passed and I stood comfortably next to him at the sink, watching him fill the bottles with the already mixed milk.

We went out to the barn together ánd he handed me one of the bottles. The lambs were about ten weeks old—white and soft and absolutely enchanting. They pulled eagerly at the bottles, flicking their tails as if by clockwork.

2

'Oh, Ian, they're wonderful. What are you going to do with them? I wish I could have one.'

He laughed. 'You can if you want to.'

'But we haven't got a field. How much land do they need?'

'People keep horses in the middle of London. You've got a garden. If there's not much grass you just have to feed them more concentrates.'

I would gladly have sacrificed the flower beds and the herb garden to have a lamb of my own.

'What about Gerald?' asked Ian. 'Would he mind a sheep in the garden?'

I realised I had forgotten all about Gerald in my enthusiasm. Gerald would mind very much. Gerald, who spent his days dressed in a suit lecturing to history students at the Polytechnic in the County town; Gerald, who liked life to be precise and ordered—everything pigeon-holed: one cat and one dog in a house, flowers and vegetables in a garden, sheep and donkeys in a field. We indeed had one cat, a sleek black creature with yellow eyes named Christabel, but I had already upset the equilibrium by collecting three dogs and allowing a large grey rabbit to hop about the house using a litter tray near the back door and chewing holes in the bottom of the curtains and the corners of the carpets. A sheep eating his dahlias would definitely not be popular. Personally I hated dahlias but, for some reason I could not understand, Gerald had a great fondness for them.

'Yes, he would mind,' I said sadly, 'he'd bring it straight back to you.'

Ian laughed again and I envied him what seemed a blissful existence surrounded by fields and sheep.

I decided there and then that I was going to have sheep, too. Not hundreds, as Ian had, but a few as pets, to wander around an orchard and sit with me under the apple trees. The next day, without saying anything to the rest of the family, I began touring the estate agents' offices and put my name on all their mailing lists.

Two weeks later I was standing in an overgrown garden looking at a little Tudor house with honeysuckle climbing

3

over the roof. It was only four miles from the village where we lived but on a little-used lane surrounded by fields. The house was empty and there was a key in the village with a caretaker, but it had been mislaid—borrowed by some other prospective purchasers and not returned. However, I was content to peer through the windows and wander round the garden.

The house leaned at all angles. Through one of the windows I could see a heavily beamed ceiling. There were two large fireplaces and some little doors with eighteenth-century hinges. The garden was large, with a big thatched barn in one corner, and behind the garden was a two-acre meadow. It was perfect.

I walked up the side of the meadow which was sown with barley. The ground rose behind the house, and when I reached the hedge at the top and turned to look back, the house seemed to shelter in a hollow. Only the old, undulating roof and upstairs windows were visible. The whole house had a peculiar list at one end, leaning towards the hedge as if to peer over it into the lane.

It was surrounded by tall trees: old grey-green willows behind the barn and tall, straight poplars in the hedge, with the sound of the sea in their leaves. Crickets were chirping in the hedgerow and the yellow-green barley shimmered in the heat. There was not another house to be seen anywhere, nor any sound of human habitation. No cars passed along the lane. Away to the north were blue-grey hills—the East Anglian Heights.

I lay in the dried grass at the edge of the field. I could have a sheep and some chickens and bees, and lots of apple trees. I would fill the meadow with cowslips and moon daisies, stitchwort and campion and beautiful grasses—wild oats and rye, hare's tail and cat's tail, cloud grass, quaking grass and timothy grass.

I returned to the garden, wading through the long grass and the overgrown rose bushes. There was an enormous old lilac bush near the kitchen window, and I saw a little grey and white cat watching me from under it. She sat quietly, her white paws neatly together, her tail curled

4

round them. Behind her, moving backwards and forwards cautiously, were two smaller cats—a little grey tabby and a small brown cat with ragged fur and a scrappy tail. They were very thin and looked ill.

'Poor little things, you look as if you're starving,' I said. 'Did your owners leave you behind when they moved?'

I went back to the village. Gerald was in London for the day at a seminar and I could not contact him. I phoned the estate agent and found that they had several people interested in the house, the price of which had now gone up by offers. I made him an offer and said we would go into the office the following morning. I asked him about the cats, but he was not interested. He believed there were some strays there, but it was nothing to do with him: he was simply selling houses.

I could not wait for Gerald and the children to come home and see the house. The hot afternoon seemed endless. The dogs were lying in cool, dark corners, growling at anyone who went too near. The sun burned down, sapping my energy but not my enthusiasm. I was filled with excitement at my discovery.

Tom was home first, rushing in through the open front door, singing happily. His thick, light brown hair was tousled, his socks rumpled. What a good-looking boy he was, I thought, with his deep blue eyes, the colour of anchusa flowers, and his determined features—so like the brother I adored. I adored Tom, too, and his lovely sister, my daughter Katy. A less than happy marriage had given me two beautiful people who would always be my friends, as I hoped I would always be theirs. The most important thing about being a mother, I felt, was to be first of all a friend.

Tom was in his last term at the village school. In the autumn he would join Katy at the comprehensive school in the town eight miles away. He had a very amiable disposition and the gift of winning everyone over to his point of view by his extrovert nature and his cheeky grin. 'Tom likes to play the clown,' his form teacher had written disapprovingly on his last school report, but she had told us

5

at the parents' open evening that he was a very likeable child and, somehow, however naughty his escapades at school and his practical jokes, he usually managed to charm his way out of serious punishments and the wrath of the headmaster.

Now he dumped his school books on the kitchen table and took some gingerbread out of the cake tin while I made some tea.

'How was school?' I asked.

'All right, I suppose, but a bit hot. We had to practise for sports' day this afternoon. Don't forget it's next Wednesday.'

'Of course not. I'm going to win the parents' race.'

Tom laughed. 'Like last year! All my friends said you'd fall over your long skirt, but you beat all the others, and Mr Ledbury.' Mr Ledbury was the headmaster.

'That's because I took my shoes off. He should have done. I'll beat him this year, too. You see.'

'Miss Jones asked if anyone would look after the school guinea pig for the summer holidays, so I said we could. I thought you wouldn't mind. Can we look after it?' he added hopefully. 'It's a very nice guinea pig.'

'Well, I don't see why not. But you must remember to feed it and clean it out. What's it called?'

'Pudding. Oh, that's good,' he said, helping himself to another piece of gingerbread.

'Have you got any homework?'

'Not much. I'll do it later. I'm going out to see my garden first. I'll bring you some radishes. Come on, dogs,' he called to the hairy trio who had been sharing his cake, and disappeared into the garden, the dogs running happily after him.

Katy was home about half an hour after Tom. She came in carrying heavy bags of school books and a large art folder. Katy's ambition was to go to art school, of which Gerald disapproved. But I thought she had great talent, as did her art teachers, and encouraged her as much as I could.

As a little child she had been enchantingly beautiful with an almost doll-like quality. Now she was growing into a lovely young girl. She had a perfect oval face, with smooth, pale skin and large blue eyes with long lashes. Her thick, dark hair was cropped short, with wispy curls on her cheeks and long strands at the back on which she threaded beads and tiny bows at the weekends.

She spent most of her spare time drawing shoes or making clothes, and in the evenings heavy metal music echoed from her bedroom while she struggled with physics and chemistry homework. The combination of pop music from Tom's room and the sound of Hawkwind from Katy's often had Gerald tearing at his already thinning hair.

Gerald arrived home a couple of hours later, to the scent of lavender and the strains of Vivaldi's *Four Seasons* which I had playing in the hall. He sank thankfully onto the chesterfield, while I made him a coffee.

'How was your day?'

'Tiring. London was oppressively hot. The pavements were red-hot; the parks were full of people lying about on the grass or sitting in deckchairs.' He looked tired, I thought, and suddenly older. He took off his glasses and put his hands to his eyes as if to brush away the heat and the dust. I was so used to his face that I seldom really looked at it. Now, sitting opposite him beside the open window, with the summer scents of the garden drifting in as a perfect compliment to the soothing strains of music, I found myself looking at him, as if for the first time in years. Yes, he did look suddenly older, his hazel eyes tired and rather sad, and I felt a pang of guilt. What had gone wrong all those years ago? Why had Gerald married me, when maybe he would have been much happier with someone more conventional? Someone who would have settled for a warm modern house and an ordered life, instead of moving through a succession of old houses, with mice, spiders and draughts along with the beams and old-world charm. Before moving to this fifteenth-century house we had lived in a thatched Tudor cottage. Each time was to be the last, perfect move, but always I found somewhere else where I wanted to live more, and now I was about to try and persuade Gerald to do it all again.

'I had forgotten how beautiful it is out here,' he said. 'As I drove home from the station the fields looked so green and fresh, the air smelled so good. I don't know how people work in London every day, let alone live there. I would hate to live in a town now. What have you been doing today?'

'Well . . .' I hesitated. 'I went and looked at a cottage just out of the village. It's all on its own, surrounded by fields, and so beautiful. You can't believe how wonderful it is, and there is a little meadow with it as well.'

'But we don't need a meadow.'

'I know you'd love it if you saw it. Won't you just have a look at it? In any case, I found some stray cats there, and I want to take them some food.'

Gerald smiled then. 'You and your old houses. I believe you'd collect them if you could. This house is so beautiful and about the oldest house you'll find. There is plenty of room for us all. We don't need to move again.'

How could I explain about Ian's wonderful lambs, and that I longed, needed, to have one of my own? Suddenly the sight of all the other houses around was irksome and I wanted to be surrounded by fields and sheep. I wanted to hear only the song of skylarks, the wind in the trees and the distant hum of tractors; not the chatter over neighbouring fences and children playing in nearby gardens.

'Just come and see it. It's so perfect.'

'My darling, if it was about to fall down, you probably wouldn't notice, so long as there was a thatched roof and lots of beams, and a wildly overgrown garden. I suppose you are planning to get a donkey or some beast to put in the meadow.'

I laughed at him, but he was right. I never noticed such essentials as rotting window frames and leaking roofs. What mattered was how I felt about the house itself. Old houses were almost like people to me—they liked you and attracted you, or repelled and turned you away.

'All right, we'll go and look at it after supper, but I'm sure it will have lots of things wrong with it. So don't set your heart on it. Remember some of the cottages you have

8

wanted us to buy, and think what a mistake they would have been.'

We had supper on the terrace at the back of the house. I collected some food and bowls and a bottle of milk, and then we piled into the car and set off up the road. The children were eager to see this place I had described with such rapture. Tom was already planning tree houses and expeditions.

The cats were asleep under the lilac bush. The grey and white cat and the small grey tabby came up to the bowl and began to eat hungrily, but the little brown one hung back. We moved away and it crept forward and began to eat weakly. It seemed to be on the point of starvation and I feared that it would not survive. When we put some milk down it could scarcely lap. It was very wary of us, watching us all the time while it ate.

We wandered round the garden and peered through the windows, and then walked up the path beside the barley, next to a field of wheat. The corn was high and rustling mysteriously. Skylarks were singing and swallows darted after clouds of little insects. Gerald liked it almost as much as I did. I told him I had phoned the estate agent and at the moment we had the highest offer on the house.

'We'll go into the office first thing in the morning,' he said. 'It's a pity we can't look inside. There are three bedrooms, are there?'

'Well it says so on the particulars, and I would imagine so. It's big enough for three bedrooms.'

We went back to the garden and inspected the barn. It was taller than the house and in a good state of repair. Privately I thought it would be ideal for sheltering sheep, though Gerald no doubt saw it as a garage.

The cats had finished their food and I gave them some more milk. There seemed to be an unspoken agreement that we would look after them from now on.

The next morning, after Katy and Tom had gone to school, we drove to the market town ten miles away, where the estate agent had his office. There was much discussion and several phone calls. As I feared, there were other prospective purchasers—one actually waiting in the outer office as we came out. It was agreed, however, that if we could get a bridging loan and sign the contract within a fortnight, the house was ours. The agent had another key to the house, which we took, and we went back to look inside, taking some more food for the cats. They came forward from under the lilac bush as we got out of the car and ate hungrily.

'Now let's see what we're buying,' said Gerald, turning the large key in the old lock. The door creaked and opened into a room with a dark-beamed ceiling. It was in the centre of the house, with windows looking onto the lane and the meadow. There were several doors opening off it, one of which contained a staircase.

There was a large fireplace at one end of the room. A small coke-burning stove sat incongruously in the middle of the brick hearth. We could have an Aga there to make bread and soup, and to sit beside in the winter and keep my lamb warm when she came. Another door revealed a lobby with a bench and hooks for coats and a back door, and leading off this was a bathroom. At the other end of the house was a sitting-room with another large fireplace. The ceiling was very low and had one large, central beam. In one corner Gerald could not stand upright, but if we took the plaster down to expose the beams it would give more height to the room.

We went upstairs. The room above the sitting-room was large and light. The other rooms were enchanting, with sloping, beamed ceilings and little windows in the roof. Everywhere needed painting and the plumbing was rather antiquated, but the house was in a much better state of repair than I had expected. I could not wait to move in. I wanted to be there already, but now we had the problem of selling our house in the village, and all the legal turmoils and delays that moving brings. We went home and Gerald drove off to see the solicitor and the bank manager.

From the size of the timbers and the general construction, I put the date of the house at about 1580, certainly pre-Civil War. It was very like the thatched Tudor cottage we had lived in before our present, older house. I had a great fondness for thatch, besides its picturesque look. It was warm in winter and cool in summer. But I was prepared to settle for old peg tiles.

Late that afternoon I had a phone call from the estate agent who had been in contact with our solicitor. He confirmed that our offer to buy the house had been accepted. It was really going to be ours.

When Gerald came home we all went back to the house with a picnic supper for ourselves and the cats. The children were eager to look inside and choose their bedrooms. The upstairs floor sloped at all angles: the largest bedroom had a difference of one foot in level from one side to the other. The bedrooms with the sloping ceilings were next to each other, one leading off the other. The end room was the smallest and was reached by climbing over a tie-beam about eighteen inches off the floor. The doorway was small and had a little pine door, shaped to fit. Tom decided he wanted this room. Katy wanted the one at the other end, so Gerald and I were left with the one in the middle. I had liked this room best, so I was pleased. It had a window looking out onto the barley field, soon to be an orchard. In my mind's eye I could already see the sheep there, wandering about under the apple trees.

We took our picnic up to the top of the meadow and sat under a large oak tree. The distant hills were misty. I loved those rolling blue hills on the Cambridgeshire border: how often I had walked over them among the sheep and the mullein and the song of skylarks. Now I would be able to come to the top of the meadow and see them whenever I wished. I could pretend they were the moors of Yorkshire where I was born, or the gently rolling heather-covered hills of the Border counties of Scotland, or the blue hills of Wales. There was not another house to be seen. We could be anywhere in England.

We began feeding the cats every day. It became a kind of pilgrimage and a kind of good luck charm. I felt that if I did not go to them every day, something might go wrong with the sale of the house and we should lose it. After a few

weeks I became attached to them for their own sake and not just because I was sorry for them, and I decided that if the sale did fall through I should bundle them all into cat baskets and take them back to the village. After about two weeks a fourth cat appeared—the most scruffy, straggly looking cat I had ever seen. It was tabby striped, but its fur had a dull red tinge to it, and its tail looked ragged and chewed. I assumed that we now had a complete family: the grey and white cat must be the mother and the two smaller ones her kittens; this, I thought, was the father.

I had already called the little brown cat Ursula, meaning 'she-bear', which seemed to suit her. We decided to call the new cat Barrington, and the grey and white cat Mittens. After some deliberation we agreed on Alice for the small grey tabby.

Then it was August and the children and Gerald were on holiday. We sat in our new garden and listened to the whispering of the poplars. They rustled even when there was no wind. We lay on the mown prunella and yarrow that passed for a lawn, in the hot sun, thinking about our orchard of next year, the chickens and the sheep. I had already decided to call my sheep Pandora, when she arrived, so I told the children the story of Pandora and her box full of all the evils of the world.

'That's not very nice,' said Gerald. 'You can't call her Pandora if she's going to bring all those evils.' He viewed the prospect of a sheep with much less enthusiasm than I did.

'But it wasn't her fault. It only means that she was curious. Anyway, she was the first woman in the world, and as she will be our first sheep I think it's quite appropriate. I think it's a lovely name.'

'I like it,' said Katy. 'At least it's different. She will probably leave her evil all over the kitchen floor,' and they all laughed.

My brother Rodney and his wife Melissa came to stay with us for the weekend. Rodney was several years younger than I and as a child I had loved him dearly, protectively. Now in his thirties, he had grown into a handsome, strong-willed man, tall and fair with blue eyes, and had become my greatest friend.

He was a petroleum geologist and had been working for an American company, partly in London and partly in America. He had met Melissa there, a delightful girl from Texas with a lovely southern accent, and brought her back to live with him in England. She was young and pretty, with fair hair and blue eyes to match his. Together they made a very attractive couple, radiating happiness and love. Rodney and I had always been very close: he was godfather to Tom and Katy and would always have a special place in my life. I was very fond of Melissa and could not have chosen a sister-in-law I would have liked better if he had asked me.

Melissa loved our quaint villages scattered round North Essex and Suffolk, and was fascinated by our ancient houses. I had told them on the telephone about the prospective move and now they were taken to Monk's Green to inspect the little farmhouse and our cat family.

Rodney was over six feet tall and he found the low ceilings rather daunting. 'Mind your head!' I had to shout hurriedly as he went through the little doorways from one room to another. When he got to the sitting-room there was nowhere for him to stand upright. I told him that we were going to expose the ceiling beams and that we had also decided to have the floor lowered. Apart from the fact that, in his eyes, the house seemed to have been built for a family of dwarfs, he liked it and thought the situation ideal.

The plumber and the builder arrived and large mounds of yellow clay appeared outside the sitting-room window. Inside it looked as if giant moles were in turmoil. However, there was soon a smooth new concrete floor a foot lower. When we had new pipes and radiators everywhere the workmen departed, leaving mounds of sand and rubble and trampled plants.

Gerald decided to start on the sitting-room ceiling. We had exposed ceiling timbers before and knew only too well the dust and dirt it created. Besides the plaster itself, the space behind it was often filled with chaff. He began at one corner. The beams underneath were quite large and un-damaged. After he had exposed three of them it became obvious that at one end of the room they were not sup-ported. We could put our hands round the ends between them and the wall. They were being held up partly by the plaster and partly by the large elm floorboards that were nailed to them upstairs. We had some old timbers behind the barn, so they were hurriedly fetched and used to prop up the ceiling. The bottom sill of the house had rotted, causing the end wall to drop and pull outwards; that accounted for the way the house leaned towards the lane and the difference in floor levels upstairs. By the end of the day, all the plaster was down and the beams each end of the room were propped up with bricks and timbers. But it was a beautiful ceiling.

Moving day finally came, with all its chaos. We lit a fire in the sitting-room and sat round it in the evening with mugs of coffee, and listened to the owls. It was a lovely feeling to be there, surrounded only by the fields and the trees. The next morning was the beginning of a perfect September day. There was a fine mist on the meadow and glistening spiders' webs covered the hedges.

A few days later I went to see Ian again. We stood by one of his fields, leaning on the gate and watching the sheep grazing steadily across the pasture. Most of his sheep were Cheviots, white, soft-fleeced sheep with gentle faces and Roman noses. He also had about thirty Jacob sheep—shaggy brown and white beasts with rather daunting look-ing horns. He had started his Jacob flock with some ewes from Maidstone zoo.

'I saw your house was for sale in the summer,' he said.

'That's why I've come to see you, to ask if I could have a lamb in the spring, an orphan, to bring up on a bottle.'

'Lizzy, you're crazy,' he laughed. 'You haven't moved just for a sheep, have you?' He seemed thoroughly amused by the whole idea. His blue eyes lingered on my face and I was suddenly aware of his closeness beside me. I turned away and concentrated my gaze on the sheep grazing near us. 'You can certainly have a lamb if you want one,' he continued, 'but it won't be till March. Do you want a Jacob?'

'I like Jacob's wool best for spinning,' I said, 'because of the colours, and it is so lovely and soft. But I really want a white sheep. One that looks just as one imagines sheep.'

'That's easier. We always have some Cheviots to bottle-feed. I thought you'd want a Jacob, but I have a smaller flock of those and we don't usually have any needing bottle-feeding. The Jacobs are better milkers.'

'Do you use the milk? Make cheese or something?' I had been reading about the continental East Frieslands, and about Roquefort cheese made from ewes' milk.

'No, I just mean they're good mothers, and the lambs feed better. Often the Cheviots will simply reject the lambs. It doesn't necessarily mean the ewes have died. Why don't you have a ewe now, and then see it lamb in the spring?'

It was a tempting thought. I could hardly wait for my sheep and March seemed a long way off. I could put her in the car and take her home now. But our field was still brown furrows and I thought of a pregnant ewe rushing wildly round the garden terrified of us and the dogs. I knew nothing about sheep and contemplated lambing with some trepidation.

'The field's not ready yet,' I replied, 'and I thought if I brought it up on a bottle it would be really tame and used to the dogs. Could I have a ewe lamb?'

He laughed again. 'I will certainly save you one.'

I bought a book on keeping sheep and waited for the spring. The book was rather alarming. Sheep seemed to have an infinite variety of mysterious ailments, all causing sudden death. I read it over and over, as my friends read cookery books and novels.

I learned all the different sheep terms—ewes and tups, tegs and hoggets. Bottle lambs were cade lambs, or tiddlin lambs, castrated males were wethers. I tried to learn the old shepherds' way of counting—a mixture of Gaelic and Latin—and went round muttering 'yan, tan, tethera, methera' to myself.

We continued painting the house and I began digging a

corner of the half-acre garden ready to plant vegetables. The house was warm and cosy with the Aga now installed, and the cats, which Gerald had insisted should live in the barn, soon made themselves comfortable indoors. Barrington suddenly began to get rather large and produced a litter of kittens, but it seemed too late to change her name.

The days grew greyer and shorter. I loved the brown fields and the dark trees and our little house in the middle of nowhere with its view of the blue hills. I had been to the Middle East, I had been to Africa. I had lived there for a year when I was nineteen, and at the time I had loved it passionately—the heat and the dust and the very smell of Africa. But now I would not have left the England of November for anything. I was at times impatient for spring—impatient to see our brown meadow turn green and grow lush and thick. I was impatient to have Pandora and the chickens. I wanted to plant the apple trees and grow rows of vegetables and herbs. But I loved the grey mysteriousness of November, the magic twilights and the dreaming trees.

In the week after Christmas the weather changed and the New Year dawned cold and crisp. It was a bright day with an icy breath. While we had breakfast we discussed what New Year resolutions we were all going to make. Katy was going to do her weekend homework on Friday night, instead of leaving it until Sunday afternoon. Tom was going to practise his violin more.

'Well,' I said, 'I'm going to be a vegetarian. I don't mind about the rest of you, but I don't want to have to cook any more meat. If you want meat you'll have to have it at school or at work.' I had tried it so many times before. I had stopped eating meat myself, but had to go on cooking it for Gerald. I expected opposition. But instead he simply smiled and said,

'All right, if that's what you want to do, I don't mind.'

'How can we have a pet lamb and eat someone else's?'

'I know how you feel,' said Gerald, 'you've been on about it for years. I don't mind giving it a try, but I'm sure it will mean a lot of extra cooking for you.'

Rodney and Melissa had given me at Christmas, among other things, some herb seeds and a packet of alfalfa for sprouting. I had been growing it on the draining board in a jam-jar for the last five days, so it would be part of our first vegetarian menu. The alfalfa had a pleasant nutty taste to it: we ate it with potatoes in their jackets cooked in the Aga. The children were both in favour of the idea. That first week we had a far greater variety of food than usual, and discovered that lots of vegetables, besides being better uncooked as far as nutrition went, were also nicer to eat in their raw state; that parsnips thinly sliced in rounds like potato crisps and fried (in vegetable oil, of course), were infinitely preferable to boiled or roasted ones, and there was an endless variety of seeds that could be sprouted in jars and eaten in salads or sandwiches. I experimented with sunflower seeds, frying them in oil and then sprinkling them with salt, and found them so delicious as to be addictive. The children had always liked yoghourt, so I stocked up on lots of large pots, and on different varieties of cheese. At the end of the week they decided that the experiment had been fun and they were all, including Gerald, in favour of continuing.

The first week of February was unusually mild. Then it began to rain. It rained for days on end, until the drive was a sea of mud and the lawn as water-logged as a soaking sponge. The ditch in front of the house was full to overflowing and some branches had fallen across it, giving it a waterfall. We had a moated Tudor farmhouse now.

The river down in the valley was swollen and flooding, spreading out like a lake over the surrounding fields. The cold, clinging dampness made spring seem so far away. Both spring and my lamb seemed always just out of reach. The sky was steely grey and full of rain. It was hard to tell where the sky ended and the earth began—only stark trees dotted the dampness.

At last the sun came out, and the celandines covered the banks with their bright golden stars. The birds began singing in the early morning. March had finally arrived.

One morning Ian phoned. He had a lamb, if I still wanted

one, that had been born the night before. It was not a ewe but a little ram lamb, but I did not care. I would have a ewe as well later on.

Tom was home for half-term and busy in his bedroom painting model aeroplanes. I called up to him.

'Tom! Ian's got a lamb. Do you want to come and fetch it with me?'

There was a thundering of footsteps and he tumbled down the stairs.

''Course I do. Are we going now? I'll go and open the gate,' and he was already out in the garden before I had found the car keys from the hook in the kitchen.

When we arrived at the farm Ian was in the lambing sheds. They were large airy barns, the floor covered with straw and an all-pervading smell of sheep. I took a deep breath: it was a wonderful smell. The barn was penned off in sections. There were some rotund ewes sitting together at one end, obviously waiting to lamb, and little pens with ewes and lambs together.

Ian took us to one side of the barn, to the individual pens where some white Cheviot ewes were penned up with their lambs. He picked out a lamb from one of the pens. It had been standing disconsolately in the corner while another lamb was feeding from the ewe.

'What happened to his mother?' I asked. I did not like to think that she had died, much as I wanted her baby.

'Oh, she's all right. That's her there. She rejected him because she was having twins and while she was having the second lamb another ewe came up and licked him. So then he smelled different and she wouldn't have any more to do with him. Then the second ewe produced twins as well, so she won't have enough milk for three.'

He handed me the lamb. It was quite large, bigger than I had expected. It lay quietly in my arms. I thought it was the most beautiful lamb I had ever seen. I could hardly believe that it was going to be mine to take home. Ian gave me a large bag of milk powder.

'Oh, he's so beautiful, Ian. Thank you so much. Will he be afraid of the dogs?'

'No, he's not old enough yet. Feed him in about an hour's time.'

Tom got into the car and I put the lamb on his knee, and we drove home slowly. Ian waved as we disappeared, standing in the barn doorway, looking amused. Tom sat very still, transfixed by the novelty.

'Isn't he lovely,' I said. I felt so happy. I wanted to sing, to run all over the green fields and shout to the wind that I had the most beautiful thing in the world.

'Yes,' said Tom, his face shining with excitement.

'Let's call him Adam.' It seemed a fitting name for our first lamb and for something so perfect. Now I was glad that we had all become vegetarians. It would not change the world, it would not help the thousands of other lambs; but there would be one lamb that would not go the way of all the others, one lamb that would be loved like the dogs and allowed to die a natural death.

We put a cardboard box with straw in it by the Aga and put him into it. He stood up and flicked his tail. Our three dogs—a spaniel of uncertain temper, a black labrador and a large yellow wolf-like creature—went forward slowly and sniffed at him and the two bigger ones were despatched to the garden. Sophie, the spaniel, went sidling up to him wagging her tail and then sat down next to his box. We had several kittens and one of them had been sitting on the dresser watching everything that was going on. He jumped down and walked over to inspect the new arrival. Sophie rushed forward and bundled him away, then returned to sit beside Adam's box. She had adopted him. He jumped out of the box and went up to Sophie. He seemed to like her, too. I mixed up some milk for him and he took it from the bottle quickly and eagerly. I had thought he might object to the bottle but the milk was gone in a few seconds. He then settled himself in the straw and went to sleep, lying with his head across his front legs.

The big dogs were let back inside. They peered over the edge of the box and then went and lay down under the table. Tom and I spent the afternoon watching Adam and giving him more milk.

Katy's bus trundled to a halt at the gate. She came up the path with her heavy bags of books and I rose to make her some coffee as she opened the cottage door.

'Hello, Katy, had a good day?'

'Not really,' she said, dropping the bags on the tiles. 'Why are you smiling like that? What have you been up to, Mother?'

She turned and looked at Tom sitting by the Aga, and then spotted the cardboard box. She ran over and peered in at the warm, white bundle.

'Oh, how lovely,' she said. 'Is that Pandora?'

'No, it's a little ram. I'm going to call him Adam.'

'Did Tom go with you to fetch him? I wish I could have come, too. Did his mother die?'

I told her what Ian had said to me about the ewe rejecting him.

When Gerald came home I was sitting on the settle by the Aga with Adam on my knee. He smiled at my excitement and felt the lamb's soft wool and agreed that he was beautiful. Despite his earlier misgivings he was as captivated as I was.

'How lucky we are to have him,' he said. 'Not everyone has the opportunity to have a lamb like this. Are you pleased with him? Are you happy?' Yes, I was ecstatically happy.

I mixed up some more milk, but Adam did not seem to want any this time. My book on sheep-keeping said that more lambs died from overfeeding than underfeeding so I was not unduly worried. He had taken quite a lot of milk during the afternoon, so I assumed that he was simply not hungry. The milk just ran out of the corner of his mouth. He seemed so sleepy, but we thought he was tired after his strange day. He was very young, only about fourteen hours old. He spent the evening asleep on my knee, wrapped in a blanket. He felt warm and heavy. I tried to feed him again about ten o'clock, but he still would not take any milk. I felt slightly apprehensive, but I put him into his box with the straw and the blanket and tried again at midnight. But he would not suck at the bottle. The milk just trickled out of the side of his mouth. Now I knew that there was something very wrong.

'He's going to die,' I said to Gerald, 'I'm sure. He's just been getting quieter all evening. He should be hungry by now. What are we going to do?'

'I don't think there is anything we can do. Perhaps he's just too small.'

'It's not fair, he mustn't die. What have I done? That's the proper food Ian gave me.' It was too dreadful. He looked so peaceful lying there in the straw as if he was just very tired, but I felt he was slowly slipping away from me and I did not know what to do.

'We'll have to phone the vet. We can't just let him die.'

Gerald shook his head. 'It's no good, I don't think he will be able to do anything. I don't know what's wrong, but I'm afraid it's too late.'

I dialled the familiar number to find out who was on call. It was Will. I had been told that he knew all there was to know about sheep. I had seen him a few years before on television performing an operation on a sheep. I could not now remember what the operation was, only that it had been Will doing it. If anyone could save my lamb, I was sure that he could.

22

He explained at length about newborn lambs, and that if they did not have enough colostrum (which was the first milk) from their mothers when they were born they would die. They did not have any antibodies and simply could not survive. They just faded away as Adam was doing and there was nothing to be done. He said he had tried before with antibiotics and drips, but always they died. The only thing to do was to put hot water bottles round him and try and raise his body temperature well above normal. But he lay so still, gradually getting weaker and weaker, his breathing fainter and fainter until finally it stopped.

I felt desolate. I felt that by bringing him home I had killed him. I went to the top of the meadow and sat under the oak tree and cried. To be given something so perfect and have it taken away again so quickly was unbearable. I buried him near the house and covered the little mound with primroses.

I phoned Ian the next morning and told him what had happened. He said there must have been something wrong with him, and as soon as he had another lamb he would let me know. But I felt very responsible for the fact that Adam had died and decided that I would not dare to bring another lamb into the house, even if Ian offered me one.

But after a couple of days I could think of nothing else but having another lamb.

'I must have a lamb,' I said to Gerald. 'Where can I get one? Could you go to the market and get me one?'

'Ian will let you have another one. Just be patient.'

'But he must think I'm not capable of looking after one.'

'Don't be silly. Of course he'll give you one.'

I thought about stealing a lamb. The blue hills that I could see from the top of the meadow were covered with sheep. I could drive up there and bundle one into the car without anyone knowing. I began seriously to wonder if I would be able to take one undetected. In my saner moments I wondered how the rest of the family put up with me.

I went to see Will and ask him about sheep.

'I feel it must be my fault that he died,' I said sadly.

'You mustn't feel that,' he said. 'If they do not have

enough colostrum they do not have any antibodies, so they just cannot survive. One wonders why the ewe rejected it anyway. Perhaps she knew there was something wrong with it.'

I told him what Ian had said about the other ewe licking him and changing his smell, but Will seemed to think that was too simple an explanation.

'Would it be safe to have another lamb, do you think?' I asked. 'Could it have caught something from the dogs?'

He smiled. 'Pick a strong, healthy-looking one next time,' he said.

Adam had looked strong and healthy, but he had still died. I did not understand about sheep.

Chapter Two

It was a long, miserable week. It rained incessantly. I longed to go and see Ian. I would have spent the whole of that week in the lambing sheds with him, sitting with the sheep and lambs, watching them, just being with them. I wanted to go and hold all the lambs and be near them. All I could think about was having a lamb.

On Friday evening I took Tom to Castle Monkton, our nearest village, about three miles away, for his weekly violin lesson. Tom's teacher had two large cats, a very handsome tabby and a fat, slothful ginger cat which looked as if it should be in a story book. It was a friendly creature and had lately taken to sitting on my lap during the lesson while I sat and listened to Tom. It spread itself over my skirt and began purring with half-closed eyes, looking utterly contented. The violin has always been my favourite musical instrument and the warm, orange body of the cat and the silvery strains from Tom's playing were soothing and peaceful. By the end of the hour I felt happier than I had all week.

On our way home I nearly ran over a hare. It suddenly appeared out of the blackness in the middle of the lane. I braked quickly and it sat up, motionless in the beam of light from the car headlights. Then a second hare jumped down the grassy bank and joined it. In a minute they had bounded away into the dark fields. Beautiful hares, my good luck charms. Perhaps I should have another lamb after all.

Ian phoned up the next morning.

'Hello, Lizzy,' he said, 'do you still want a lamb? I've got several sets of triplets and the ewes have trouble feeding three lambs as they only have two teats. You can come and choose one of them if you want to.'

'Oh yes, Ian, please. Are they Cheviots, too?'

'No, they're Jacobs this time—all ewe lambs.'

'How soon can I come over?'

'Whenever you like.'

'I'll come straight away—I'll be there in about twenty minutes.'

I had not originally wanted a Jacob lamb, but now I did not care. I would have had a three-legged lamb—anything. Gerald was working that Saturday, but both Katy and Tom were at home and they rushed out to the car, Katy demanding to have the lamb on her knee on the way home this time.

When we reached the farm Ian was in the lambing sheds as usual. The ewes with the triplets were penned up next to each other. The first ewe had three little black and white spotted lambs standing round her, all about the same size. They were smaller than the Cheviot lambs, but Ian had said previously that Jacobs were always smaller, even as singles.

The next pen contained an enormous old brown and white ewe with a pair of horns and long, shaggy fleece. She stared at us with unfriendly eyes. Two lambs stood next to her, and the third and smallest was lying in the straw in one corner. Ian moved it with his foot and then pulled it to its feet. It stood shakily, looking rather dejected. For some perverse reason I always choose the small, pathetic looking creatures—the puppy that is sitting in a corner away from all the others, the chicken that is being pecked, the kitten that nobody wants. And of course, I wanted this lamb.

Ian picked her up and gave her to me. She was so small and light. Adam had felt warm and rounded and quite heavy. But she was bony and thin. I held her against me.

'She is so small, Ian. I'm half afraid to take her. She won't die, will she?'

He just laughed. 'I have every confidence in her,' he said, 'or I wouldn't give her to you. These lambs have been having their mother's milk for four days now, so they'll be

26

all right. Don't worry, you'll be surprised how quickly she will grow.'

I wrapped Pandora in a blanket and Katy sat proudly in the front seat, holding her on her knee. I drove home slowly. She was the smallest lamb I had ever seen. 'Choose a strong, healthy-looking one,' Will had said, so I had picked the weediest lamb that I could see. Half-way home I wondered if I should turn round and take her back. It would be too awful if she died as well. How many times since I have thought of that day, and how glad I have been that I did not take her back.

We arrived home and carried her into the house. I had made up another box by the Aga and I put her into the straw. The dogs came up and sniffed at her. Sophie, the spaniel, looked at her, then turned her back and stalked off to her basket. She had taken a fancy to Adam but Pandora obviously did not have the same appeal for her. She was not going to mother this lamb.

Poor little Pandora. She was so small and she looked quite bewildered. She jumped out of the box and went to the corner of the room, standing between the old settle and the fireplace with her back to everyone. She did not under-stand why she had been taken away from her mother and she looked so unhappy. I made her a bottle of milk but she would not take it. I tried for some time, letting the milk trickle into the side of her mouth. She kept swallowing every time her mouth was full, so I could see that some of the milk was going down, but she would not suck from the bottle. I wrapped her up in the blanket and sat down by the Aga with her on my knee. She seemed comforted by the warmth and finally went to sleep.

One of the kittens appeared and sniffed at the straw box. Then he climbed in, curled up and went to sleep. Pandora seemed to be about the same size as him, but with longer legs.

I tried her with the bottle again at tea-time, but although I had warmed the milk and held her close to me so that she would feel as if she was next to her mother, she did not want to have any. I tried for about half an hour and the milk trickled in slowly, being swallowed down every time her mouth was full. But still she would not suck at the bottle.

In the end I began to feel rather desperate and phoned Ian. He said it was just that she had been used to suckling from her mother so obviously she would not like the bottle. He was sure that she would have some eventually when she was hungry. He told me to ring again in the morning if I was still worried. But the morning was a whole twelve hours away and I did not know whether she would last that long.

Later that evening, Gerald came in as I was trying to give her some more milk. He stood and watched as I struggled to get the milk into her, this time with a little more success. By holding the bottle under my chin and putting my arm over her back, I managed to get her to take some milk herself. She pushed her nose up into my neck as if she was pushing against her mother.

'Hello, Pandora,' he said, 'you *are* a tiny lamb.'

'Oh, Gerald, I can't get her to feed properly. I've been trying all day, but she doesn't seem hungry. I phoned Ian and he said it was because she's been used to having her mother's milk and won't like a bottle to start with. But I'm so scared she is going to die, too.'

'I'm sure Ian must have thought she would be all right or he wouldn't have given her to you. She's so pretty, more like a little calf than a lamb.'

'But what am I going to do if she won't have any milk?'

'She's had a little now. She's very small, so she probably doesn't need a lot at once. Try her with some more in an hour or two.' He smiled encouragingly. 'Don't get yourself upset about it. I know it was awful that Adam died, but perhaps there was something wrong with him anyway. I'm sure she'll be all right. You always worry about the animals too much. Would you like some coffee?'

He made two cups of coffee. I wrapped Pandora in a blanket and we went into the sitting-room and sat by the fire with her. She went to sleep then. She lay very quietly and I wondered if she would die, too. She did not move but lay with her head stretched out along my arm. I sat with her

28

until after one o'clock in the morning, but I was so tired I kept falling asleep. Finally I made up some more milk, and after she had reluctantly taken a little, I put her into her box and went to bed.

I woke early, as the sky was beginning to lighten, and lay in bed listening for any sound downstairs. But it was very quiet. I was half afraid to go down in case I should find her dead, but I wanted to see if she was all right and what she was doing. Suddenly I heard a faint bleating coming from the kitchen below. When I opened the stair door she was standing in the middle of the floor looking around her. She turned when she heard me, her black ears sticking out each side of her head like bats' wings.

'Hello, Pandora,' I said, 'are you hungry?' She followed me across the kitchen, and I made her up some milk. After one or two false starts, she took the milk quite well. She did not finish all that was in the bottle, but she had considerably more than the day before.

She was enchantingly beautiful, and I could hardly believe that she was mine to keep. It was also hard to believe that she would grow so large. Her mother had looked huge. At the moment she was the size of the kittens, but by the end of the summer she would be bigger than our labrador.

Her back was mainly white with black spots and she had a wide black patch each side of her face, like a panda, and black ears. Her nose was cow-like and, as Gerald had said, she looked more like a tiny heifer than a lamb. She trotted round on little pointed feet, slipping slightly on the tiles.

Having finished her breakfast she went over to the large dog basket and sniffed at it. Then she stepped in and sat down, folding all four feet up together rather untidily and collapsing in a heap. I should have liked to weigh her, but although she was not very big she was not really the right shape to fit on the kitchen scales and we did not have any others.

I fed her again in the middle of the morning and at lunchtime, and she seemed quite hungry now. After lunch we went into the sitting-room and sat by the fire. It was a cold, blowy March day, and although there was a lot to be

29

done outside—clearing ditches, cutting hedges and digging in preparation for putting in the vegetables, we decided to spend Sunday afternoon by the fire. Katy and Tom sat on the floor playing chinese chequers, and Gerald buried himself in one of his archaeology books. I sat with Pandora on my knee and she soon went to sleep. She seemed happier today, as if she was beginning to get used to us all. She did not feel quite so small, either, although she could not really have grown overnight. I suppose I was getting used to her as well. She had survived the first night with us and I hoped now that she would grow strong and healthy.

After a week Pandora began to fill out. When I had first brought her home her neck was flat and thin, like a piece of cardboard, but now it was rounded and felt strong. She had grown used to her bottle and was always ready for her milk. She would push her nose up into my neck and flick her tail as if it worked by clockwork. She was having five feeds during the day, the first one at about six o'clock in the morning. She now ran to me bleating as soon as I went downstairs in the morning, asking for her breakfast and pushing impatiently against my leg.

I bought her a little pale blue cat collar with a bell, which was exactly her size. The dogs were very good with her, especially the labrador. Sophie was inclined to grumble if she went too near, but the big dogs took little notice of her. The kittens pretended that she did not exist, but they liked her box of straw and spent most of their time asleep in it. Pandora, on the other hand, preferred the dog basket and she would go and sit in it when she had finished her bottle, folding all her legs up under her and sitting with her head on one side, watching everything that was going on.

One morning she went to the basket and found it completely filled by the labrador's large black bulk. She stood there for several minutes, staring in, wondering what to do. Eventually she stepped in carefully, lifting her feet over Henry's tail and legs. She then crumpled up and sat rather awkwardly half on top of him. He did not move but looked rather embarrassed. He tried to wag his tail at us, but

31

Pandora was sitting on it. He put his head on his front paws instead and pretended to go to sleep. He was a wonderfully patient and good-natured dog, but terrified strangers who stopped at the gate by standing with his front paws on it and barking furiously.

Pandora was the most inquisitive creature I had ever seen, so her name had been well suited. Everything had to be sniffed and inspected and nibbled at. As soon as the pantry door was open she walked in to see what was inside; if I opened a cupboard door or the bottom of the dresser, she pushed her head in. Her favourite game was to chase the broom when I was sweeping the floor. She would hop about in front of it and nibble at the handle, and would skip about all over the floor, getting in the way.

Rodney and Melissa had gone to Texas for two weeks. Rodney was in charge of the London office of the American oil company for which he worked, but often commuted between London and Dallas, sometimes going one day and coming back the next. They were selling their house west of London, and had been looking at cottages in Suffolk to be nearer to us. As soon as they returned from America, they came to see us and to inspect the newest member of the family.

Rodney was mildly amused to see me cuddling a lamb wrapped up in a blanket.

'You should put her in a pram and push her round the village,' he said.

'Oh, she's so pretty,' said Melissa, cuddling the tiny bundle of wool. 'She's so small, but she doesn't really look like a sheep.'

'No,' I agreed, 'I think it's because she is black and white. She looks more like a little calf.'

Rodney told us that while he was in America he had given in his notice to the oil company and had decided to go and live in America. He felt that there was more space, more opportunity. Texas was four times the size of England with a quarter of its population. For the price of our two acres he could buy twenty and build himself a house to any specification he liked. Outside the towns there were no building restrictions and no such thing as planning permission.

I felt very sad that they were going to leave England. There was a time, perhaps, when I might have contemplated going abroad, too, but not now. Now I would not have left England for anything and I wondered how Rodney could bear to leave it all—the trees and the greenness, the fields, the little villages, the age and the history. But they would not be going just yet. He had a month to work in London and then they were going to rent a cottage in our area for the summer and go to America in September or October, so we should have all summer to see them.

Meanwhile Pandora was growing quickly. She followed me everywhere and trotted round the garden with the dogs. No doubt she thought of herself as a dog, too. She was particularly attached to Henry, the labrador, and would walk beside him, pushing against him. He walked slowly when she went with him, wagging his tail, slinking a little and looking slightly foolish.

She seemed to gravitate towards black. We had a black woolly hearth rug that looked like a sheep and when I shook it out she would run up to it. Perhaps black to her was a herd colour. When the dogs ran barking to the gate, she ran with them, but whereas they ran towards an enemy, it was obvious that she was running instinctively away from one. They ran in aggression and she ran in fear.

She began jumping about and would leap high in the air, landing facing a different direction. She seemed to enjoy an audience and would have us all in fits of laughter at her antics. The more we laughed, the higher she jumped. She also took to jumping up onto the settle beside the Aga, and would sit there all evening, her legs folded neatly under her, watching us with her dark eyes with their long lashes.

Gerald brought home a large sack of sheep nuts and a bale of hay, but she refused to eat them. I tried mixing the nuts with some of her milk and giving them to her on a teaspoon, but she spat them out.

A few days later I was dismayed to find that one side of the spaniel's face was hard and swollen out like a tennis ball. I phoned the veterinary surgery to make an appointment and drove to Wetherbury with her, a distance of some seventeen miles.

'She has an abcess on her face,' said Will, feeling the lump gently and looking inside her mouth to see if it was from one of her teeth. There was a hole on the inside of her cheek.

'We'll have to get it to drain outside,' and he reached for a syringe to draw off some of the fluid.

'I'm sure she'll bite,' I said holding her collar with one hand and putting my other hand around the end of her muzzle. She kept very still, giving little complaining yelps, but she did not growl at all or make any attempt to bite. She was always so naughty at home, and so good in the surgery. When Will had drawn off some of the fluid he found another syringe and a phial of antibiotic.

'How is her temper now?' he asked, filling the syringe and stabbing my friend in the back. She sat still and said nothing.

'Pretty nasty at the moment,' I replied. 'I expect she's jealous of the lamb now, as well.'

'How is the lamb?'

'She's growing quite well and is so friendly. She follows me everywhere.'

Will smiled. 'They can become very affectionate. Sheep are not as stupid as people imagine.' He counted out some tablets for me and wrote on our record card. He had small, neat writing.

'Give her one twice a day, starting tomorrow.'

'I'm not sure what to do with the lamb next. I've got her a bag of sheep nuts and some hay, but she won't eat them.'

'Sheep learn by copying others. But she will. Get her outside now. It's a mistake to make too much fuss of them. Sheep become humanised and forget they're sheep. You'll never keep her out of the house.'

'But I want her as a pet. She couldn't be as difficult as Sophie.'

'Don't say you haven't been warned,' he replied. I was soon to find out just how right he was.

But she was so easy to love, so trusting and somehow so vulnerable. I found it psychologically disturbing that she would normally have been bred for meat. Those first few weeks I had nightmares that she was being herded into a transporter with lots of other sheep and driven away calling frantically to me. I would wake up with a terrible feeling of panic.

Suddenly the weather became hot and still. I woke early one morning and listened to a robin singing in our ancient apple tree whose fat pink buds were ready to open. The sky was clear, pale green with early morning. It was going to be a perfect day. Then I heard a cuckoo calling nearby, the first that year. After breakfast, when Gerald and the children had left, I sat on the kitchen doorstep with a mug of coffee and Pandora came and sat next to me. She had grown considerably since that day when we had brought her home, just a few weeks ago. I thought now, as I ran my hand over the black and white curls of wool, how foolish my fears had been. She had seemed so fragile that I had not believed that I would be able to look after her properly and had been convinced that she would die. But Ian had been right—I *was* surprised how quickly she was growing. The baby lamb's wool was so soft, the white patches in tiny tight curls, the black patches longer and straighter. There were two small lumps on top of her head, the beginnings of a pair of horns. She sat perfectly still beside me, her feet and legs folded up under her, out of sight except for the shiny black hooves just showing from under her middle.

My friend Laura arrived later that morning. She lived in a village about four miles away, not far from Ian's farm, and knew him and his wife well. Laura and I had been to the same school—a boarding school which I had detested, and I had spent most of my time there plotting escapes. Laura was several years younger than I, so I had not known her very well at school, but had met her again quite by chance a few years ago, while doing some shopping in Wetherbury, after one of my visits to the surgery with my problem spaniel bitch.

I had recognised her instantly. She had an oval-shaped face with high cheekbones and smooth pale skin. Her hair was thick and dark and she had brown eyes that lit up the whole of her face when she smiled. She had remembered me, too, and was surprised to find how near to each other we were now living. And so we had become the friends that we had never been all those years before.

We sat on the prunella and yarrow lawn, drinking coffee, while Pandora nibbled at the hedge.

'She is very sweet,' said Laura. 'I must bring the girls to see her. They will probably pester me to have a lamb as well, that's the trouble.'

'Well, why don't you? You've got room for one.'

'Yes, there's the wild garden that Patrick calls his vegetable garden. I could do with something to keep that tidy. We have thought sometimes about getting a goat—but I don't know. What about holidays?'

'I could look after a lamb for you. I don't want to go on holiday. I would only choose somewhere like this, surrounded by fields and sheep, so I might as well stay here with mine.'

'What does Gerald say?'

'He'd like a fortnight in Rome looking at the ruins, so I'm trying to persuade him to go,' I replied, laughing. 'Actually, he likes Pandora and is surprised how affectionate she is. Pandora—' I called to her and she turned her head and then came running across the lawn, skipping and jumping on her tiny pointed feet.

Laura laughed. 'She is lovely, I must say. We saw Ian last night in the Woolpack. He asked if I'd seen you lately and how the lamb was getting on.'

'You can tell him she's wonderful. The most beautiful animal I've ever had.'

I picked her up and she pushed her nose against my neck. 'She's so warm and she smells so lovely. I've been trying to house-train her. I think she's getting the idea. I have to keep watching her but I can usually get her to the door in time. At least the droppings are small and solid and easy to sweep up.'

36

Laura laughed again. 'I do believe you're quite crazy. That's probably why I like you.'

Next time I went to Wetherbury to do some shopping and collect some more worm tablets for the cats from the surgery, I decided to look at the hills just outside the town that I could see from the top of our meadow. I drove through the lanes lined with cowslips and stitchwort, the pale fields turning green and sloping away to the distance.

The bright sunlight shone through the newly green branches of a larch wood. In a field beside the wood I saw some brown shapes running, and stopped. They were hares. They ran backwards and forwards through the young barley shoots. I saw one running up the lane behind me—its sooty-tipped ears pricked, listening for danger. When it was within twenty yards of the car it stopped and sat still for some minutes in the middle of the lane. Then it turned, leapt easily across the rough grass at the side of the lane and raced down the barley field to where the other hares were still running about.

An old man was standing beside the gate of a little cottage opposite the wood. He was watching the hares, too, and he smiled as I approached.

'They are beautiful,' I said, 'I love to see hares. I could watch them all day.'

'There are six of them in that field. They've been there all morning. It's the mating season, you know, that's why they're so lively. Some people say they do a lot of damage, but I don't know.' He grinned. 'I like to see them myself.'

Four hares eat as much as one sheep, I had been told. I thought of Pandora. Hares and sheep, they were always together in my mind. They belonged to the hills and the moors, the empty tracts of land, the places I loved best. The old man looked towards the hills.

'Look at that view. Many people would pay a lot of money for a view like that.'

'Yes, they would,' I agreed, 'it's lovely. This is a beautiful place.'

'They wouldn't want it in the winter, though. It's cold then and bleak. The wind comes across these hills.'

I had seen the hills covered with snow, dotted with black trees—desolate and empty. Where did the hares go then? No warm burrows for them. They could only crouch in the snow with icy fur and trembling paws.

'I don't know why they go abroad for their holidays,' continued the old man. 'Why go away from England when you can have all this?'

Why indeed? England is so beautiful and this part of it was as beautiful as anywhere. I thought again of Rodney and wondered how he could bear to go.

I picked some stitchwort from the edge of the lane. The starry white blossoms were everywhere. To pick stitchwort, it is said, is to run the risk of being pixy-led, bewitched. I had been bewitched by the hares and I had been bewitched by Pandora. I thought about them all the way home.

Pandora seemed to grow larger every day and by the time she was about eight weeks old she was taller than the spaniel and a good deal heavier. She had two horns on the top of her head, growing up stiffly out of the black and white wool. They were now about one and a half inches long and straight, and she had two more little lumps on the sides of her head. I wondered whether they would grow into horns as well, or were simply bony parts of her skull.

38

She spent most of her day wandering about in the garden, nibbling at things as she passed, and slept in the kitchen at night. She had a great liking for rose shoots and the rose bushes all looked as if they had been attacked by a swarm of locusts. We probably would not have any roses this year, but I did not mind. Gerald, I knew, was less pleased.

Now the fields were all lush green, a patchwork of varying shades, dotted here and there with bright yellow squares from oilseed rape flowers. The cowslips along the roadsides were fading, but there were buttercups everywhere. I can never resist picking them. I love the shiny petals, so bright, so unreal, as if they have been enamelled. I had pots of buttercups on the window sills, and bluebells and campions mixed in with them, and large jugs of cow parsley in the hearth. It was everywhere—in the hedges, behind the barn, large scented clumps of it filling the air with sweetness.

It never fails to amaze me every year, how quickly all the wild plants grow up and come into flower. I had planted some herb seeds in a corner of the garden—thyme and sage, dill, rocket and caraway—and while I peered at them every day and watered them and waited for something to happen, the wild plants grew up and burst into flower untended, transforming the roadsides and ditches and any waste patch, while the carefully nurtured seedlings remained specks of green.

The trees were suddenly green, as if they had all sprung into life overnight, and our old twisted apple tree was a mass of pink blossoms. The field on one side of the cottage garden was sown with beans and their scent was intoxicating. There seemed to be cuckoos calling all day long. They flew over the meadow or sat in the wild cherry trees at the front of the house, or called from the orchard two fields away.

Chapter Three

Our little house was in what might have been called a hamlet—a few scattered cottages and a farm hidden from view of each other by hedges and twists in the lane. But scatterings of brick and pottery, still turned up every autumn by the plough on nearby fields, showed that Monk's Green had once been a thriving village, and an old eighteenth century map that we inspected at the county Records Office confirmed this.

The map gave all the old field names—Great Readings and Little Readings, Coneys Fair, Mouselands, Hither Leys and Farther Leys; Stanford Shot, Middle Field and Upper Field; Willow Croft and Paradise. Some of the names were fairly explicit, others more obscure. I wondered at Stanford Shot, and Mouselands conjured up delightful pictures, like those in a child's story book.

There had been several cottages in the field opposite us on the other side of the lane, and also some in the field at one side. There had been a cobbler and a wheelwright, and one hundred yards down the lane a blacksmith, at the corner where we turned to the village of Castle Monkton, along a narrow hedgeless lane between wide, pale fields, with the blue hills away to the north and the outline of the castle ahead, which gave its name to the village.

Until we moved, only four miles and yet almost into another county, I had only been to Castle Monkton once a week in the evenings, to take Tom for his violin lessons, or *en route* for somewhere else. Now I went there to do my shopping and discovered a village of winding streets and ancient houses where the swifts screamed and swooped.

There was a small square known as 'The Ponds', surrounded by little eighteenth-century cottages, an imposing
Georgian house and some beautiful heavily timbered
medieval houses. In the eighteenth and nineteenth centuries this had been a centre for the straw-plaiters who had
worked in the cottages, their straw soaking behind the
houses in shallow ponds specially dug for the purpose. The
ponds and the straw-plaiters had gone, but the name had
survived and there were some fine examples of the intricate
straw work of the last century in the village church. There
was a little baker's shop in 'The Ponds' that made wonderful apple doughnuts to which Katy and I grew extremely
partial, and a visit to the village always had to start at the
baker's.

The ground rose behind 'The Ponds' and, on its highest
point, almost hidden by tall trees, was the castle. From a
few miles away the castle was clearly visible and stood out
on the skyline as an unmistakeable landmark, but in the
village it was possible to drive right past and never see it. It
had been built in the twelfth century by the powerful de
Veres, Earls of Oxford. Now only the keep was left standing, but it was one of the best preserved examples of its type
in England.

Less than ten miles on from Castle Monkton and we
were into Suffolk and the town where the painter Thomas
Gainsborough was born. Katy and I liked exploring
new places and sometimes we went there on Saturday
mornings, to look round the old market town with its
medieval houses and wonderful views across the river
Stour.

By moving just a few miles we had found a whole new
world.

I still went shopping in Wetherbury and took the animals
to the surgery there when they were ill. Wetherbury was a
place I had always loved. It was on the borders of Essex and
Cambridgeshire—on the edge of the blue-grey hills that I
could see from my meadow. It had little cobbled streets and
ancient leaning houses. There was a beautiful church
standing out on a hill above the town. It was of cool grey

41

stone, as far removed in time from the little Tudor cottages clustered in the narrow streets around it, as they were from our time. The floor was grey flag-stones worn smooth by the feet of centuries. On the north side the windows had plain glass—old and uneven in small, leaded panes. The sunlight filtered in, making patterns on the flag-stones, and the green leaves of the trees outside were distorted and blurred by the ancient glass. I liked these old plain windows so much better than the gawdy colours of the Victorian stained glass.

Wetherbury also had a castle, of sorts, and a museum that held a varied and fascinating collection of exhibits. My favourites were the old locks and keys and carved beams and mullions that had come from some of the medieval houses in the town. There was a piece of old plaster containing rushes, still with their feathery seed-heads. I often went into the museum to run my hand along the old pieces of wood and the smooth carvings.

I found something very reassuring in the centuries-old timbers in the museum and the medieval houses in the town. Although the people who made them had long since gone, the fact that their handiwork remained was like a testament to the immortality of the soul. Part of them lived on in their beautiful houses.

There was a large common in the town, surrounded by lime trees. At one side was an ancient maze: complicated patterns cut into the turf. At one time these mazes were numerous but sadly most of them have been destroyed. They are thought to have been pre-Christian excavations connected with fertility rites. This maze, I had been told, was the best surviving earth maze in England. Every time we went to Wetherbury, Tom and Katy always wanted to go on the maze and would have endless attempts at reaching the centre, while I sat idly in the sun on the grassy bank beside it, watching the dogs running about on the common and making love among the daisies.

The next time Katy and I made a Saturday morning expedition to Wetherbury we found a circus encamped on the common. There were various tents and caravans parked about and some ponies tethered on the grass. Right in the middle of the common was a camel. It was tethered from a rope halter and looked quite at home sitting on the daisied grass chewing its cud. It was a rather splendid looking camel, not too large, with two humps. Camels in zoos always look as if the moths have been chewing at them, but this one had a fine, thick coat of a dark brown colour.

Katy and I stood and looked at it for some time.

'Isn't it gorgeous,' I said. 'What fun it would be to have a camel in our field. I wonder if we could get one to bottle-feed from somewhere.'

'I don't think Father would like a camel.'

'No . . . probably not.' At odd times I had heard Gerald talking about camels. He said they always had unmentionable diseases. I thought the advent of antibiotics had proved a simple cure for the affliction that had killed Henry VIII, but Gerald would probably view a camel with suspicion.

Katy and I wandered round the market square. I bought some vegetables—purple aubergines, huge flat mushrooms and a bunch of watercress. Katy lingered at a stall selling earrings and bracelets and Indian clothes. She was into a blue and green phase and picked out some long silver and turquoise earrings. There was a small mirror propped up on the stall and she held them up on either side of her face and surveyed her reflection.

'What do you think, Mother?'

'I like them—they suit you. I'll get them for you.'

'No, you won't—I've got some money to buy them, but do you really think they're all right?'

'Yes, I do. I'll buy you one of those silk scarves, then. Which one would you like?'

Katy fingered through the squares of silk and chose a prettily patterned scarf of pale blue and apple green. We paid for our purchases and then made our way across the square in the direction of the craft and coffee shop. Katy bought some cards of cat drawings surrounded by borders of tiny brightly coloured flowers and then we sat at one of

43

the little round tables in the window to have our coffee and a large piece of sticky-topped gingerbread.

Between Wetherbury and Cambridge was a small zoo that I knew kept some rare breeds of sheep and llamas.

'Do you fancy a quick visit to Milton zoo, before we go home?' I asked Katy, my mind still on the splendid brown beast on the common. 'There might be some camels as well as the sheep.'

Katy laughed. 'All right, Mother, so long as you promise not to take a camel home with us. I know you.'

The zoo had some Hebridean sheep, black multi-horned sheep with tiny lambs at foot. The ram had enormous horns—one pair on top of his head curling slightly forward, and a large thick pair at the side curling round towards his face. There were some small brown creatures with a strange mousey smell that I thought might be some species of deer, but the label on their enclosure called them Soay sheep. They were as far removed from Ian's flock of Cheviots as a Cairn terrier from a bulldog.

There seemed to be a dearth of camels, but we found the llamas. The thought of all that lovely alpaca to spin was exciting, but close up the llamas were really too large and hideous to go with sheep. When I mentioned them later to Will he said that the zoo was on his list of clients and that he trimmed the llamas' feet with difficulty. They were extremely ill-tempered and could spit in one's eye at fifty paces.

Pandora was now nearly three months old. She had long since outgrown her cat collar and now had a large collar like Henry's, on which was inscribed her name and address. She still slept in the kitchen at night and spent her days wandering about the garden. She had been weaned from her bottle and was eating grass and chewing her cud like a real sheep.

She was so friendly and so tame. If I called to her in the garden there would be answering bleats from behind a bush or the corner of a flower bed. I always knew where she was. She came into the house to chew her cud. The front door was left open all day and she hopped up the steps and

44

settled herself in a corner of the kitchen or sometimes in the dog basket. She now filled it completely and she sat there chomping her jaws up and down in a slow, steady rhythm.

One afternoon Tom and I went to see Ian. I wanted to ask him about trimming Pandora's feet, and also to see how she compared for size with his lambs. It was a still, hot day towards the end of May. The fields along the lane were dancing with heat. When we got there the sheep were all gathered in the yard at the back of the lambing sheds and Ian was in the middle of spraying them to discourage the flies. The ewes had been shorn the day before and looked strangely thin, like Mediterranean goats. The lambs were running about with the ewes—a lot of white Cheviots, bigger and heavier looking than Pandora, and some black and white Jacob lambs that looked about her size. There were also half a dozen completely black lambs. At least they were dark brown. Black sheep are never really black and even black cats look brownish in the sun. Ian straightened up when he saw us and hailed us in his easy, friendly way.

'How are you getting on with the house-training?' he asked me. He had heard from Laura that I was trying to house-train Pandora and she had reported that he was greatly amused.

'Well,' I said, 'she has the idea, I think. Sometimes she goes out, but sometimes she doesn't.' I had to admit it was not an easy task. If I was watching her I could get her outside quickly, but often I had to go round with a dustpan and mop.

'Oh, Lizzy,' he said, shaking his head and laughing.

I had intended to get another lamb from Ian in August, before they were sent away, but seeing them all there now it was very tempting.

'I want another lamb some time, they are so lovely,' I said, watching a batch of them being drenched in spray.

'Well, have one now while they're here and you can see what you want. They will be going back to the fields after this.'

Tom chipped in eagerly.

'Oh, yes, do get one now. Go on.'

'Do you think I should? Which one of them can I have?' I asked Ian.

'Whichever you like. Choose one.'

When I had first collected Pandora I had thought of getting a Cheviot as a second lamb, to be like the first beautiful Adam who had died. But now I thought of having another Jacob like Pandora. Somewhere in this milling crowd were her mother and her two sisters. Then the black lambs caught my eye. I have always rather liked the look of black sheep. They are cuddly and bear-like.

'I don't know. Perhaps a Jacob.' I was torn by indecision. 'The black ones are rather fun.'

'Oh, do let's have a black lamb,' said Tom. 'What about that one?' and he pointed to a sturdy-looking ewe lamb standing near us.

Ian advanced with his crook and there was a thundering noise as the sheep ran wildly round the yard. He cornered the lamb Tom had chosen and turned her onto her side. She had a nice face with golden-brown eyes like dogs' eyes. Her wool was shorter and thicker and she was more stocky than Pandora, with a broader face. She panted and looked frightened.

'She's a Jacob-Cheviot cross. I can show you how to trim their feet now on her.' He took a penknife from his pocket and cut away a small sliver of hoof along the outer edges of her feet.

'Hers don't really need doing yet, but you have to keep an eye on their feet. They can get overgrown. It's just like cutting your nails. Just trim away the horny outer edge as it grows up so that it is level with the soft part in the centre.'

Ian picked up the black lamb and carried her into the sheds. She looked very heavy.

'Will she and Pandora be all right together? What should I do with them? They won't fight, will they?'

'No, they'll be fine. You won't have any trouble. In a couple of days she'll be really tame and docile.' I hoped he was right.

We put a collar and lead on her that I had in the car and she kicked and bucked like a rodeo pony. Ian put her in the front of the car and Tom sat there holding her collar. She seemed very large now that she was in the car and I wondered if she would rampage. I drove home slowly, hardly daring to breathe or change gear, but she did not move at all. The lane was very winding and the three miles between Ian's farm and our house seemed like twenty.

Rodney always followed the oil share prices every day in the *Financial Times*, and I had started watching them as well. One company for which Rodney predicted success was Berkeley Exploration, and that was now the first name for which we looked every morning. So I thought it would be rather fun to call the new lamb Berkeley and, if I had known at the time how many explorations she would make, out of the meadow and up the lane in search of adventure, I could not have chosen a more apt name for her.

Pandora had a pen on the back lawn, and if I went out during the day I sometimes left her in there when the weather was fine, instead of shutting her in the house. She was standing in the pen now and as soon as she heard our voices trying to coax the unwilling Berkeley round to the back of the house to join her, she bleated loudly.

Berkeley bleated back, overjoyed to hear a familiar sound. She trotted round the corner of the house and ran forward eagerly to meet one of her own kind, in this strange new world. But when Pandora saw her she froze with horror and her eyes opened wide. She did not like the look of Berkeley at all. She was used to cats and dogs, but not other sheep.

With difficulty I lifted Berkeley into the pen: she was amazingly heavy. She ran up to Pandora, but Pandora tried desperately to get away from her. She pushed at the netting and tried to jump over it. I climbed into the pen with them and she ran up to me and stood behind me, peering round my skirt like a shy and nervous child. I had not expected this reaction and did not know what to do with them. Pandora was not afraid of great big dogs, but another sheep terrified her. So I sat in the middle of the pen with them, and after watching for a while Tom went off to do his

47

homework. When Gerald came home I was still there. He liked the look of Berkeley immediately and did not seem in the least surprised to see her. I had mentioned that morning at breakfast that I thought of going to see Ian. Now he simply said:

'I knew very well that if you went up there you would come back with another lamb. I knew you wouldn't be able to resist them.'

'But what are we going to do with them? Pandora is really frightened of her?'

'That's ridiculous. She's not afraid of dogs like most sheep are, but to be scared of another sheep—I've never heard of that before. Just come out and leave them. They'll be all right.'

I climbed out and Berkeley ran up to Pandora, but she ran wildly round the pen again, pushing at the netting. She caught one of her horns in it, and some blood trickled out from the base of the horn and down her face. I remembered what Will had said to me: she did not know that she was a sheep.

I got back in the pen with them. The dogs had been watching with interest, and Henry, the labrador, went up to the pen and sniffed through the wire. Berkeley decided he looked more friendly than Pandora and went up to him. He was black like her sister. He wagged his tail and she stood by the wire with her nose touching his.

We decided the only thing to do was to leave Berkeley in the pen and have Pandora in the garden and let them get used to each other at a distance. I lifted Pandora out and she ran off behind the lilac bush and began pulling crossly at the rose bushes, tossing her head and snorting a little. Poor Berkeley stood sadly in the middle of the pen and bleated. Henry lay down beside the netting and stayed with her for some time. She quietened down and began to eat some grass. But when he moved away from her she began to bleat again. She needed a flock.

She spent an unhappy night and we had a sleepless one. The pen was under the bedroom window and she bleated on and off all night. I wondered if I should take her back to

Ian in the morning. Perhaps they would never be friends. I had been told of a bottle lamb who had refused to join a flock when he was older but was quite happy to live in a field of horses.

First thing next morning the dogs and Pandora were let out of the kitchen into the garden. Pandora trotted off to a corner of the garden to help herself to breakfast off the hawthorn hedge, and Henry went round to the back of the house to see Berkeley. He seemed to like her. She decided she had had enough of the pen and pushed her head under the wire and managed to wriggle out. Her explorations had begun.

She hesitated for a moment, watching Pandora eating, but decided that Henry was more friendly and trotted after him. When Pandora was small she had followed him everywhere and now he accepted Berkeley in the same way. She kept with him like a shadow all day. It was a beautiful sunny day and he spent the afternoon asleep in the sun outside the front door. Berkeley sat next to him, actually touching him, and chewed her cud. She seemed remarkably quiet and unworried, considering she had only arrived the afternoon before and the whole environment was so totally different. She did not run away from us, although she kept just out of reach. During the afternoon we made a pen in the barn for her and that evening we got Henry to lead her into the barn. She stood for a few minutes and bleated, then sat down in the straw and seemed quite happy.

Pandora had kept well away from her all day and made it quite clear that she wanted nothing to do with this strange new creature. The horn that she had caught in the netting was now at an angle and I wondered whether it would eventually fall off.

The next day was Sunday and we decided to take the dogs for a walk along the lane in the morning. Berkeley was much tamer and allowed us to stroke her head and rub her between the ears. It was a hot, still day. The air was scented, the lane full of seeding grasses and little butter-flies. Pandora usually went on these walks as well, so we

thought we would take both lambs and see what happened. Berkeley trotted along next to Henry, keeping very close to him. Pandora watched her from the corner of her eye and kept a good distance, but the lambs stopped every now and again to nibble at the grass, so we all stopped. Nothing came along the lane to disturb our strangely assorted pack: a large yellow wolf with Tom, a black labrador with Gerald, a fat black lamb with Katy, and a black and white lamb and a ginger spaniel with me.

The two lambs were very different shapes. Berkeley's back view was square and solid, with two stocky back legs well apart and a short tail. Pandora's legs were longer and thinner, so that in fact she was slightly taller, though not so wide, and she had her tail left long. It reached nearly to the ground and she kept swishing it as she walked along, and tossing her head. Her wool was much longer and softer than Berkeley's whose coat was short and thick and oily. In fact she did not look very lamb-like at all. She looked just like a fat little sheep.

It was remarkable how she had simply accepted her new life and fitted into it. I have no idea what she thought of it all, but as long as she was with Henry, she seemed to be happy.

By the end of Berkeley's first week with us she and Pandora had become reasonably good friends. She began to make explorations all over the garden into all its awkward and unsavoury corners. And she took Pandora with her. There was a path, now overgrown, round behind the barn, and they would disappear at one side and reappear at the other festooned with strings of goose-grass that took ages to pull off their wool. They would vanish into a ditch full of nettles, their thick coats impervious to the stings. I chased them out, rubbing my ankles, cursing and looking for dock leaves.

Berkeley's explorations took them into the onion bed and they nibbled all the tops off the onion sets. They both seemed to have a liking for onions. They invaded the herb garden and ate all the chives. One of their favourite plants was jack-by-the-hedge which has a strong smell of garlic.

They were always coming into the house to chew their cud, smelling very strongly of onions. They also gobbled up all the raspberry canes and strawberry plants.

Pandora was good and dainty and well-behaved, but Berkeley was big and bold and somewhat perverse. There was a faint green haze over the meadow now where the grass and clover seed had germinated, but for the moment the lambs had to stay in the garden. Berkeley, however, was forever trying to push through the hedge and get into the meadow. My most frequent view of her was a large woolly bottom fast disappearing. Her head was small in comparison with the rest of her, but she seemed to think that if her head would go through a hole the rest of her would, so she pushed and pushed until it did. I was always going into the field with Henry to lead her back to the garden. As soon as she saw him she would run after him: he was obviously her new flock leader. The holes in the hedge were hastily blocked up with wheelbarrows, garden spades and anything else that came to hand until they could be properly mended.

But Berkeley was a very amiable creature. She wandered in and out of the house with the dogs or Pandora, and would come up to us to have her head rubbed between the ears. She had got used to sleeping in the barn on her own and trotted in there every night when it was getting dark, to have the bowl of sheep nuts I put in the straw for her. Pandora still slept in the kitchen at night, but Gerald thought it was time she joined Berkeley in the barn. So one evening she was led out to the barn and put in the pen with Berkeley.

She bleated pathetically, but Gerald was firm and shut the barn door. She then got angry and we heard her kicking the wall of the barn and bleating much more loudly, as if she was shouting angrily at us. I did not like to leave her there as I thought she might hurt herself, but Gerald insisted. After a while there was silence. In the morning they were standing quietly side by side and trotted out together to have breakfast off the hedge.

The pen on the back lawn was now abandoned as far as

the lambs were concerned, because Berkeley was so heavy to lift in and out. We had put netting round the garden, along the hedges, when we first moved there, to ensure that the dogs did not escape. I went round the garden boundaries again, to check that they were sheep-proof. I had to take Tom and Katy to the dentist after school, and as it was an exceptionally hot afternoon I thought the lambs would be better in the garden than shut into their pen in the barn. I left them in what I thought was an enclosed garden.

When we came home Pandora was standing near the front door nibbling at the lawn. But Berkeley was standing just inside the gate, tied to it by a length of blue baler twine. She had obviously been hoofing it up the lane and been captured by a passing motorist. I inspected the boundaries as I could not easily see where she had escaped. There was a small hole pushed under the netting in one corner of the garden and tell-tale hoofprints in the ditch on the other side.

A few afternoons later I thought she had done it again. All was peaceful and quiet: the dogs were all asleep in the sun outside on the front lawn; the cats were dozing, some

53

on window sills, one in the middle of a lavender bush, one on the top of the barn roof, some on the bank under the hedge. Suddenly I realised it was *too* quiet. Where were the sheep? A quick glance out of the kitchen window revealed nothing. I rushed outside but they were nowhere to be seen.

'Quickly, Tom,' I called, 'they've gone again. Can you come and help me find them?'

'It's all right, Mother,' he said patiently, somewhat exasperated by me and my sheep, 'they're here.'

I went back inside. I heard the steady chomping of sheep chewing their cud. Pandora was sitting in a corner and she peered at me with her head on one side. Berkeley was sitting under the table, her jaws moving and a wicked gleam in her eyes. I am sure she was delighted to have caught me out.

Chapter Four

Every evening, when Pandora and Berkeley had finished their bowls of sheep nuts in the barn, I picked up the bowls, said goodnight to them, and then pushed the heavy barn doors shut. As soon as I went downstairs in the morning I filled their bowls from the sack in the pantry and put them outside at the bottom of the steps. Then I ran across to the barn to let them out for the day. They always called out as they heard my footsteps on the gravel. One morning, as I went across to open the barn doors, I was dive-bombed by two swallows. They were flying in low circles round the garden to the barn, up over the roof of the cottage, and then back to the barn.

I opened the doors and, returning from their circuit, the swallows flew inside twittering loudly, round the barn and out to the garden again. I let Pandora and Berkeley out of their pen and they trotted across to their bowls, Berkeley in the lead, licking her black lips in anticipation of breakfast. I followed them and sat on the steps watching them as they ate. The swallows were now flying round excitedly, in and out of the barn, with a great deal of happy twittering, and I wondered if they would build a nest in there. Perhaps they nested in the barn every year. I would have to make sure that the doors stayed open for the rest of the summer.

The swallows spent all of that day inspecting the barn, sitting high up on one of the tie-beams, side by side, their little red throats bubbling with music as they talked to each other. There was something on one of the beams near a corner that I thought was a tangle of old cobwebs, but peering up to the darkened roof-space I could see that it was an old nest, and during the next few days they set about repairing it. They worked all day until it was getting quite dark and then settled for the night side by side on the tie-beam near their nest. They seemed unworried by the sheep in the straw below, and every night when I said goodnight to Pandora and Berkeley I looked up and saw the two little birds perched high above them.

Gerald came home one evening with six chickens. We had seen an advertisement in the local paper and it turned out to be a farmer disposing of a batch of battery hens. He had ten thousand birds. Some were sold to individuals like us, and the rest then went to be made into soup or supermarket frozen chickens.

They were a pathetic sight. They were only one year old, but they had scarcely any feathers on them and combs so pale that they were almost white. We had intended to put them for the time being into the sheep pen, but they huddled together in one corner of the cardboard box, looking so weak and helpless that they would be easy prey for cats. So Holly the rabbit was turned out of her exercise run and put back in her hutch, and we put them in that. It was more room than the chickens had been used to, and they stared at the grass and at us and then at all the cats which had suddenly appeared as if from nowhere, converging on the new arrivals from all corners of the garden.

Tom looked at them sadly. He had never seen chickens looking like that. I had always made a point of buying free range eggs and now I was more glad than ever that I had. I had expected them to look rather dreadful, but faced with the reality they were worse than any photographs. I explained to Tom, as I had previously to both children, about the way they were kept in tiny wire pens with no room to move, away from the air and the sunlight, a living hell to provide cheap food and money. After about an hour one of them ventured out onto the grass and began clucking excitedly. The others followed, but they picked their legs up strangely, lifting their feet slowly, carefully, as if they were learning to walk. One of them made some feeble attempts at scratching.

The next morning they were all out of the box making little clucking noises and scratching about in the grass. Tom asked if he could have charge of them and feed them. The chickens were going to be his project. Later that day one of them laid an egg, although to look at them it seemed impossible for them to do anything.

The following day they looked bolder and stronger and we let them out into the sheep pen. They flapped their wings and one of them ran after a butterfly. They had changed already and would soon grow new feathers.

I was worried that the dogs might consider the chickens a natural prey and spend most of their time trying to catch them, but after their initial interest when Gerald first brought them home, the dogs took very little notice of them.

I have always been rather fond of chickens and was glad to see them recovering as they made happy clucking noises to each other and wandered about the sheep pen, pecking at the grass and scratching about for grubs and beetles. They had a large cardboard box on its side for a temporary house, in which was a scattering of straw. They huddled into it as soon as it began to get dark and we wedged some wire netting across the opening with bricks. When Tom took it away in the morning they all tumbled out eagerly and gobbled up their breakfast.

During breakfast on Saturday we discussed what we were going to do for the weekend.

'We're going to make a chicken house, aren't we, Dad?' said Tom.

'All right,' replied Gerald. 'There's plenty of wood in the barn and I thought we could use that old cupboard that we took out of the kitchen. If we take out the drawers and put wire netting on the front instead, it would make a very good house. It will need a perch and some felt for the roof, but we'll see what we can do with it.'

'Great, I'll find the nails and hammer.' Tom liked nothing better than making things. 'Alex said he'd come and help,' he added as he disappeared in the direction of the barn, whistling happily.

Alex was the same age as Tom and lived in a cottage about half a mile up the lane. He was a delightful child, always happy and smiling and a very willing helper. He was always being called on to help with some weird project or other and he did them all cheerfully, whether it was scattering grass seed over our two acres by throwing it at random from a bucket, or running down the lane after Berkeley. When I went out later to the barn, with mugs of coffee and Mars bars for elevenses, I found the three of them busily constructing the hen house.

By the afternoon the hens had a very smart new house with a perch and nest boxes and a little door that pulled up and down. Alex had made the door, he told me proudly. The three of them carried the house round to the back lawn and put it into the corner of the pen. One of the hens walked up to it immediately and began making a great deal of clucking and squawking, soon joined by the others. Finally the first hen, after putting her head on one side and peering through the little doorway, hopped inside. We saw her scratching about in the straw. The other hens watched with interest but did not venture inside after her. I assumed that she was highest in the pecking order of the little group, and it was interesting that she had always been the last hen to go into the cardboard box at night. She would still be out pecking at the grass at dusk while the other five fluffed up together in their shanty home.

When I led Pandora and Berkeley into the barn that evening the hens were still out on the grass, staring worriedly at their new house, past their usual time for roosting. I left Pandora and Berkeley with their bowls and went back to put the hens in myself, by catching them one at a time. By some mysterious signal they had all retreated inside their new home and were huddled up together in the straw. I closed the little door. They could be shown the perch tomorrow. For tonight it was enough that they had found their way in to bed unaided.

The following evening, when the hens had gone into their new house and huddled on the floor again, I climbed into the pen and, lifting the flaps over the nest boxes at the back of the hen house, picked them up one at a time and put them onto the perch. They clucked in surprise but sat very still. Then, as I put the next hen up the first one jumped down. I spent nearly half an hour putting them up on the perch. I tried to do it as quickly as I could. I thought if I could get all six up at once and shut them in darkness they would stay on the perch. In the end I gave up, deciding to go out again when it was dark. This time they stayed where I put them.

The next evening there were two hens on the perch, so I put the others up next to them after dark. By the end of the week they were roosting on their own.

We continued chewing our way through packets of sunflower seeds and peanuts. Pandora and Berkeley chewed their way through the herb garden, the roses and the hawthorn hedge. Berkeley chewed through the telephone wire. I caught her in the act, with the curly, squiggly wire hanging out of the corners of her mouth and what looked like a smile across her face. I rushed up and retrieved the wire but it looked very mangled. There were chewed bits of red, blue and white wire showing.

'How could you, Berkeley?' I scolded.

Easily. It had been no trouble for her at all. I picked up the receiver and there were some cracked sounds and then silence. I pushed the offending piece of wire behind the curtain and wondered what Gerald would say if he found out. I should have to go down to the village in the morning to report it and hope they would come and mend it quickly.

Gerald found out while we were having supper. The telephone rang so he got up to answer it. As he picked up the receiver the chewed wire fell out from behind the curtain. He heard indistinct words interspersed with rustling sounds. He kept trying to make himself heard but it was obvious that the caller could not hear him. Angry and frustrated, he put down the receiver again.

'Who the hell did this?' he demanded angrily, holding out the wire. Tom and Katy put their hands to their mouths to suppress the giggles.

'One of those ruddy sheep of yours, I suppose,' he said,

looking at me. 'I've told you they shouldn't come into the house. The whole place will smell like a farmyard.'

The caller was persistent. The phone kept ringing and every time Gerald picked it up the pantomime was repeated. In the end he left the receiver off the hook.

'I shall have to report it in the morning when I go in to work,' he said. 'I just hope we don't get an enormous bill for repair. There can't be many people who get their phones cut off by a sheep.'

'You don't have to say that. Just say it's not working.'

'Don't be silly. Wires don't get like that all on their own.'

The following afternoon a yellow van with blue writing on the side stopped at the gate. The dogs ran out barking as a cross-faced man got out. I went down to the gate and grabbed Henry's collar, dragging him back to the house and calling the other two in. I shut them into the sitting-room and went back to the gate.

'Sorry,' I said, 'but they're safely out of the way now.'

'British Telecom engineer—I believe you have a faulty appliance.'

'Yes,' I said. 'Come in.'

Berkeley was sitting amiably beside the front door steps chewing her cud. She eyed him with interest as he passed. He gave her a curious glance and stepped into the house. He was holding a work card. 'It says something about a b----- goat eating the telephone.'

'No, it's only the wire,' I said brightly, 'and it wasn't a goat. It was a sheep. That black one sitting outside by the steps,' I added.

He looked at me with distaste, then looked at the wire. He said nothing but went outside again and spent several minutes rummaging about in the back of his van. I couldn't see why he was complaining. If telephones never needed repairing he would not have a job. Berkeley was only helping to keep him in employment, but he did not seem to see it like that. He returned with a new squiggle of wire with which he replaced the broken length and then tested 'our appliance' to make sure it was working.

'Thank you,' I said pleasantly.

61

He mumbled something which I did not catch. By the look on his face it was probably unrepeatable. When he went outside again Berkeley had vanished, obviously trotting off to find some more food. I saw him look round, but he said nothing. Perhaps he thought he had imagined it all.

Gerald must have forgiven Berkeley by the time he came home that evening, because he walked round the garden as usual and took her a biscuit. I found a nail in one of the beams and hooked the telephone wire over it so that it was out of reach. I just hoped that somehow she would not manage to chew through it again.

There was seemingly no end to Berkeley's prodigious appetite. The old doors in our house had latches, not door knobs to turn, and Henry had discovered that by standing on his hind legs he was able to open the doors by pressing on the latch with one big front paw. He was forever opening the door of the sitting-room which was barred to animals, and one day I went in there to find Pandora sitting in the middle of the chesterfield chewing her cud, with two cats asleep next to her. In the end we fixed a small bolt to the kitchen side of the door to prevent Henry opening it all the time, and Tom was made to promise not to lock people in there for fun. He was rather fond of practical jokes.

We had a large walk-in pantry with a window, at one end of the kitchen, and the same latch to the old pine door as the rest of the house. Having found his fun in opening the sitting-room door was spoiled, Henry turned his attention to the pantry door.

Katy, Tom and I had been invited to tea with Laura as it was her birthday, and we were upstairs getting ready. She had asked us to go over after school and sit in the garden to have strawberries and cream—the first she had picked from Patrick's vegetable garden (which she had earmarked as possible sheep-keeping territory).

'Don't be long,' I said to Katy, 'or she'll think we've forgotten.'

'Just coming,' she answered as I went downstairs and opened the little door at the bottom. To my horror I saw a large black woolly bottom sticking out of the pantry door and knew immediately where the head would be. It was buried in the sack of chicken food. I dragged Berkeley out and shooed her into the garden. Her sides stuck out grotesquely and she waddled down the front door steps. I did not know exactly how much she had eaten, but she could have been in the pantry for perhaps twenty minutes and it looked as if at least one third of the sackful had gone. I knew from my book on sheep-keeping that pig food killed sheep as they could not digest the copper which it contained, and assumed the same to be true about chicken food. At least she had not eaten the telephone wire again, so there was a panic call to the veterinary surgery and I told Will what had happened.

'Just keep an eye on her,' he said—that was easier said than done—'she should be all right. Chicken food does not contain copper like pig food. Just watch that she doesn't blow up.' I wanted to laugh, but it was not funny. 'Blow-up' meant 'get bloated', but when did Berkeley's bulging sides stop being normal for her and turn to being bloated? How could I tell? Perhaps she was bloated already?

'How swollen up is she?' asked Will.

I looked out of the doorway. She was sitting in her customary place by the steps, grunting a bit, her black sides spreading out on the grass each side of her. Her general shape was a big round black blob with a head at one point on its circumference.

'Well . . .' I hesitated. 'She's always fat, but she's fatter than usual.'

'Is she in any discomfort?'

'I should think so. She's grunting a bit.' I was not, I felt, being very descriptive or helpful, but I had never seen a sheep with bloat before and imagined then that it was just a matter of looking more over-fed than usual.

'You can try stroking her throat to get her to bring up the wind. Bloat is only a build-up of gas in the intestine. If she releases it herself there's no problem.'

'All right, I'll try that and see how she is.'

'Ring again if you're worried,' he said. I was worried now.

63

I went out and sat on the grass and stroked her throat. She seemed to like that and sat, half-grunting, half-panting, with a contented look on her face as if she was cudding. There were some very strange rumbling sounds coming from the vast black mound that passed for her body.

Katy appeared. She was wearing a pale turquoise T-shirt and short white skirt with flat daisy-patterned shoes like dolls' slippers. She had tied blue and green ribbons onto the tiny plaits she had made with the long strands of hair at the back of her neck. She stood in the doorway, looking at me in some surprise, as I sat on the grass beside Berkeley.

'Mother, what are you doing?'

'Berkeley's eaten lots of chicken food. Look at the size of her.'

'Oh, no. What are you going to do? Have you phoned the vet?'

'Yes. He said to keep an eye on her. Would you be a darling and phone Laura for me? Tell her we'll be coming as soon as we can.'

Berkeley continued grunting and rumbling. She gave several loud belches. Success! Pandora came round the corner of the house and looked at us all inquisitively, as well she might. Berkeley burped again. I got her to stand up and, holding her collar, led her across to the barn and into their pen, Pandora following behind. She had certainly eaten more than enough for one day. She was definitely confined to barracks until the morning, but I had no doubt that the prisoner would eat a hearty breakfast.

We eventually reached Laura's an hour late. I apologised and explained what had delayed us. She had already heard about the episode with the telephone and she laughed uproariously at Berkeley's latest misdemeanour.

'It's lucky you only have two lambs. I thought sheep were supposed to be good and gentle and stand about in a field eating grass. I thought it was only goats that ate everything.'

'So did I, but apparently not.'

'Perhaps I will stick to vegetables for Patrick's garden

after all. I complain about the weeds, but on balance they are probably less trouble.'

'But not such fun.'

We sat on the lawn under an old plum tree. Its dark red trunk was covered with bulbous protrusions and oozed amber-coloured sap, and every spring it was covered with tiny white flowers. The petals had all fallen now, but the flowers never produced any plums, only their beautiful spring whiteness. The garden was full of irises and yellow and white daisies, and it was pleasant sitting there in the warm shade, listening to the greenfinches calling 'chee-ree' from the nearby hedge.

The strawberries were delicious—the first I had tasted that year so I made a wish.

We ate our tea unmolested. Laura had no large noisy dogs like Henry and Wolf, whose faces would have been on a level with the table, watching each mouthful that we ate; and no greedy, pushing lambs demanding biscuits or bread and honey. She had one cat, an ancient tabby called Prudence, who was lying quietly, half asleep, under the shade of a lavender bush.

I wondered about the state of Berkeley's several

stomachs and hoped we should not find her stiffly on her back with her feet in the air when we arrived home.

As soon as we got back I went to the barn and looked in. Pandora and Berkeley were sitting side by side in the straw, chewing their cud. They gave muffled bleats when they saw me, their mouths full.

'Goodnight,' I said to them, 'see you in the morning.'

Chapter Five

Next morning I had a letter from the headmaster of a primary school in one of the neighbouring villages. I had known Alan for about ten years and had last seen him when Tom, Katy and I had spent a day with him and his wife during the Christmas holidays. He had written to ask if I would like to go and spin at their annual school fête as I had done before. I telephoned him to say that I should love to go, and told him about my lambs.

'How exciting. You'll have your own supply of wool now. When will you shear them?'

'Not till next year. They're usually sheared in June, but not in their first year—when they're a year old, or just over. I hope to do it myself. I thought I might go to some classes later on, but its probably very difficult.'

'It always looks so easy when one sees it done, but I'm sure it isn't.'

It was the school's centenary, he told me, so this year's fête was to be a special event. They were having Morris dancers and a Victorian fancy-dress competition and he was hoping to organise lots of events and attractions. By the time I had put the phone down I had not only agreed to spend the afternoon spinning, but had offered to take Pandora and Berkeley with me. No doubt I would regret it. They might be angelically good; on the other hand . . . I decided to worry about that when the time came.

My immediate problem was taking them to Wetherbury for their vaccinations. These were against some of the mysterious ailments that seemed to be symptomless and immediately fatal.

Gerald had an estate car which I was allowed to borrow for the occasion. I folded down the rear passenger seat and spread a large sheet of polythene over the back, which I then covered with straw. I put leads on Pandora and Berkeley and led them round to the open back of the car. Still holding their leads, I scrambled in myself and they immediately jumped in after me. I climbed out again, closed the back door and went round to the driving seat. Pandora rested her chin on my shoulder as we drove along, and looked out at the road ahead with interest. Berkeley sat down and nibbled idly at the straw.

When I reached the surgery I left them in the car and went into the receptionist. The waiting room was half full of dogs. Two of them were lying quietly, but the rest were panting and pulling at their leads and eyeing each other aggressively. I have always kept dogs, but not for the first time I wondered at the English passion to share their homes with such creatures.

'Should I bring the lambs in?' I asked Joan. She guarded the surgery rather as Cerberus, the dragon-dog, had guarded the entrance to Hades. Woe betide those who did not have an appointment.

'I should leave them outside,' she said, ticking my name off in the appointment book. 'I'll tell Will you're here.'

I went back to the car park, past beds of sweetly scented wallflowers. An old man had been hoeing the beds as I went in, now he had turned his attention to one near where I had left the car, and was standing leaning on his hoe and eyeing Pandora and Berkeley. Pandora was shouting very loudly and several other people had gathered round to look. I went to the car and opened the back, taking hold of their leads, and Pandora was instantly quiet.

'Are they lambs?' asked someone. 'Aren't they sweet.'

I sat on the edge of the car in the sun, and they stood one each side of me, while we waited for Will. The old gardener smiled and shook his head, then went back to his hoeing. He should have been used to such things.

Will came out with a syringe and a bottle of vaccine. He was a tall, good-looking man of about forty, with reddish hair, slightly balding, and a beard. He was wearing a blue shirt the colour of speedwells, and I wondered how he managed to look so cheerful after struggling with all the horrid dogs.

'Hello, Lizzy, how are you? And how are the lambs?' He rubbed Berkeley's black head. 'This is the black sheep of the family, is it?'

'Yes, this is Berkeley, who's always misbehaving. She's the one who ate all the chicken food. Before that she also chewed through the telephone wire.'

He laughed. 'I did warn you about making too much fuss of them.'

'They're lovely, though, such fun and so affectionate. Pandora's always good.' I stroked the side of her face.

'She's a four-horn Jacob, I see. The rams can be quite formidable.'

'I'll remember that, Will. Isn't it a wonderful day? Are you playing golf this afternoon?'

'Yes, my half-day today. Golf's very relaxing after a busy morning.'

'And lots of horrid dogs . . .' I said, laughing. I could never quite see the attraction of hitting a small white ball around. Perhaps the best part was rummaging about in the gorse bushes when it got lost.

'I like dogs,' said Will.

'That's lucky. There were a lot this morning.'

'Yes, it's funny – some days we have all cats, but there was only one today and fourteen dogs. Oh, and two lambs; I nearly forgot.'

When we got home I took Pandora and Berkeley to the meadow. Berkeley put her head down and began nibbling at once. She had lost valuable eating time in the car.

I let the dogs out into the garden and found my bag of wool and a crochet hook. I was making shawls from wool I had spun from some of Ian's Jacob fleeces and was selling them in a shop in Chelsea. I thought I would also take some to Alan's school fête, so decided to go and sit in the meadow with the lambs while I worked. It was too nice a day to stay inside.

69

The day of the school fête dawned with a cloudless, pale blue sky and a blackbird singing in the wild cherry trees by the gate.

The fête was being opened at two-thirty by a celebrity from Children's Television. Katy and Tom had been eagerly awaiting the day with autograph books ready. I was much more concerned about ferrying my beasts, spinning wheel and bags of wool to the village in plenty of time to have the display properly arranged. Katy was always very good at helping me set all the things out.

'I hope I've remembered everything,' I said to Gerald, pushing Berkeley into his car after the wheel, and the bags of wool and Pandora, and leaning on the back door as one sits hopelessly on an overfull suitcase in an attempt to close it. Gerald added his weight to the door and I managed to shut it.

'You *will* do all these things,' he said, somewhat exasperated, 'and then complain afterwards. You should just say no in the first place. It's stupid taking them.'

'I'm not complaining. I just don't want to get there and find I've forgotten my spinning wheel or something important. I'm sure they will be good. They like people, it will be fun to take them.'

Gerald shook his head and turned away.

'Come on, children, we'll follow your mother.' They got into the other car and we set off down the lane. It was a hot afternoon and the car windows began to steam up. I opened my window and Berkeley stuck her head out, sniffing the air and looking interested, as dogs do. Pandora stood in the middle, looking out at the road ahead and blocking my view of Gerald and the children.

We reached the village school in plenty of time and drove across the short, dry grass of the playing field, past endless bales of straw and people busy putting the finishing touches to various stalls. Alan was standing in the middle of the field waving his arms in different directions, sending small boys running about between the various stalls. He smiled as I stopped next to him and put up a hand to stroke Berkeley's black face that was peering out of the window.

70

'Hello, Lizzy, I'm so glad you could come. I like him. What's his name?'

'He is a she, and she's called Berkeley, as in square, and she is—very.'

Alan bent forward and looked in through the car windows.

'It looks a bit of a squash in there. Did they enjoy the ride?'

'Yes, I think so. It makes a change for them. Where would you like us to go?'

He indicated with his hand: 'We left you a space over there. Do you want any of the boys to help you set things out?'

'I think Katy and I can manage, thank you. Some straw bales would be useful, though. Could they bring us a few over?'

We parked the cars and unloaded. The sheep had leads on their collars and I put the ends under the leg of my stool. They nibbled at the grass for a few minutes, then Berkeley sat down next to the stool. Pandora hesitated, then sat down next to her.

The boys brought us some straw bales and Katy and I made a display stand with half a dozen of them—two bales high at the back and a single bale to end at the front, and covered them all with a large piece of hessian. We then set out the various items, draping the shawls over the top bales. I had brought several Jacob shawls and two made from white Cheviot wool dyed with plants. One was in several shades of pink and blue, from elderberries and blackberries, and green, from wormwood; the other was in varying shades of gold, yellow and brown, extracted from dandelion flowers, tansy and fennel, and poplar twigs. Next to them we stood a chart with colour samples—ninety different shades in all, from ordinary garden and hedgerow plants. On the lower bales we put hats and mittens and baby bootees, and little knitted sheep. A small crowd began to gather round as we set out the things.

'Look at the lambs,' people kept saying, 'aren't they sweet? They're so good. Are they pets?'

71

'Yes, they're four months old. That one's a Jacob sheep—' I pointed to Pandora. 'I had her when she was four days old and brought her up on a bottle. When she was eight weeks old I bought the black one to keep her company. They just wander round the garden and come into the house looking for biscuits. They're used to people and they like going out. We take them for walks with the dogs sometimes.'

There were lots of oohs and aahs from the little crowd. They stood round in a half-circle, but keeping a little distance from the lambs, as they might from a strange dog. I realised then that most people had never been so close to sheep before, and had only seen them as white dots half-way across a field.

I rubbed Berkeley's head between her ears.

'Do they bite?' asked someone.

'No, they're quite safe. They don't have any top teeth, anyway, just a hard plate of bone to chew against.'

'Well, I never knew that,' said an old man.

A middle-aged woman in a dark red Indian skirt, with a cotton shawl over her shoulders, stepped forward and knelt on the grass beside Berkeley, stroking her smooth black face. Berkeley sat very still, quite unworried, as if she went to a village fête every week.

'They are lovely,' she said. 'What are you going to do with them?'

'Well, nothing really,' I replied. 'Just keep them till they collapse of old age and bury them in the orchard.'

'You're not going to eat them?'

'Heavens, no! I don't eat meat, anyway.'

'Oh, you're a vegetarian? So am I. I don't know how people *can* eat them. They're so gentle and beautiful. I think it's awful.' She kissed Berkeley's black nose. 'These two are lucky, but all the other little lambs out in the fields will be killed. You see them everywhere at the moment, all so happy, skipping about together. Everyone complains about killing baby seals, but what about baby lambs?'

The other people moved away a little. Some looked

72

embarrassed, but most had blank, expressionless faces. No more vegetarians among them, I imagined.

'I wish you lots of joy with them,' she said, then turned to look at the chart of dyes. 'What beautiful colours. How do you dye the wool to produce them?'

I explained about treating the wool first with a mordant (a chemical such as alum or chrome), to make the dye fast, and then simply boiling up skeins of wool in a large pot with flowers or leaves.

'Most plants give some colour, although most of them are green or yellowish shades. Red and blue are more difficult to obtain.'

'Have you used woad at all? That gives blue, doesn't it?'

'Yes, I haven't tried that yet. That's more difficult, I think. You have to leave it to ferment first before you can get any colour out of it.'

'They're lovely soft shades, just like the old medieval paintings. I must have one of your shawls,' she said. She chose the pink and green one and I wrapped it up for her.

'Thank you so much, I have enjoyed meeting you and your lambs.'

I gave her a card with my name and address on.

'Do come and see them again if you want to. Just give me a ring.'

She said goodbye to Pandora and Berkeley, giving Berkeley another kiss on the top of her head.

I sat at my wheel and started spinning. More people came up and stood watching.

'Oh, look!' said one woman to a small boy. 'They're making wool out of sheep's doings.'

I heard several women referring to Pandora: 'Look at the ram with its horns.' I kept explaining that she was a ewe, and that in breeds of sheep where rams had horns, the ewes mostly had them as well; and that a lot of breeds of sheep were polled—that is, hornless—in which case neither rams nor ewes had horns. But I felt they were only half listening. They knew better in their own minds. Rams had horns and ewes did not. That was how to tell the difference, from a distance at least.

73

'Weaving, are you?' asked an unattractive, obese man in baggy trousers and braces.

'No, spinning,' I said.

'I'll have a pair of socks when you've finished my pull-over,' and he laughed loudly and prodded an equally fat woman next to him. 'What d'you make of that, Maud?'

'Innit marvellous,' she said.

A young, fair-haired man approached, festooned with black leather shoulder bags and carrying a microphone.

'Hello,' he said, 'I'm Martin Turner from Chelmsford Hospital Radio. We're doing a programme for the patients to listen to tonight. Could you talk to us and tell us what you're doing?'

Well, I thought, sitting here making wool out of sheep's doings and thinking how stupid most people are.

'That's an old spinning wheel, is it?' he continued.

'No, it's a new one. It came from Scotland, from a firm in Fife that makes them. But it's the same design as the old ones. There are various different types—this is known as the Hebridean.'

'Right. Can I have your name, please?' He prattled into his microphone and then I tried to explain the process of spinning, which was really so simple there was very little to say. So I went on to talk about Pandora and Berkeley and thought the patients would find Berkeley's explorations more entertaining to listen to with their supper than the mechanics of spinning.

No sooner had the roving reporter gone than the photographer from the local paper appeared. However, I knew him, and his familiar face was a welcome sight.

'Hello, Pete, I'm glad to see you.'

'Hello, Lizzy, what have you got with you this time?'

'Meet Pandora and Berkeley. Pandora's the spotted Jacob and I had her as an orphan to bottle-feed. They're being very well behaved, thank goodness. Gerald said they'd run amok and I shouldn't bring them, but they don't seem to mind at all.'

'They'll make a lovely picture for the *Gazette*. Can you move a bit nearer them? That's right. Let's have some of the children in the picture, too. Who wants to be in the paper?'

Berkeley was suddenly surrounded by several small children who obviously thought she looked safer and more docile than Pandora.

'Smile . . .' Pete clicked the camera several times.

After he had gone I had a long talk with a delightful middle-aged Dutch woman who said that she also kept a few sheep as pets and did some spinning. It turned out that she lived in Castle Monkton and we exchanged names and telephone numbers. I promised to go and have coffee with her the following week, to meet her sheep.

Katy came back with a large lump of candy floss, followed by two of her friends. 'We got his autograph,' she said excitedly, waving the book. 'Tom and Father are just coming. Tom's having a go at the rifle range.'

'Could you stay with the sheep while I go and have a look round? I won't be long.'

'Yes, of course. There are some good plant stalls.'

'Thanks, Katy. Don't let anyone touch my wheel.'

'Don't worry, Mother,' she said. She was used to standing guard on such occasions, but this was the first time there had been sheep to watch as well. They were still sitting and chewing their cud, so I thought it would be safe to leave them.

I made off in the direction of 'Bowling for a Pig': I fancied taking a piglet home with me. Will had said they made very intelligent and affectionate pets. They were clean and easily house-trained. I could have a pig indoors, sitting watching television with me. He had offered to find me a piglet to bottle-feed, but when I had mentioned it to Gerald he had firmly said no.

'We don't want a pig.'

'You mean *you* don't want a pig,' I replied.

However, if by chance I won a piglet at the fête, that might be different. I found the bowling run but was dismayed to find that the prize was not a live, squealing piglet but a large ham. I turned away very disappointed, feeling somehow cheated. I wandered round some craft stalls, and

76

chatted to Alan who was delighted that so many people had turned out for the fête and that it was such a beautiful, sunny afternoon. I bought some lavender and santolina plants from a stall and then went into the flower tent. There were some beautiful displays of delphiniums, and the air was heavy with the scent of Madonna lilies. Coming out again, I began to make my way back to the lambs and my spinning wheel. I heard a lot of shouting as I passed the beer tent, and smiled to myself. The beer tent was always the most popular place at the local fêtes.

As I neared my place, I heard Pandora calling. When I reached her I saw Katy sitting on the stool with a worried expression on her face and Pandora standing next to her shouting loudly. Berkeley was nowhere to be seen.

'Where's Berkeley?' I asked.

'I don't know,' said Katy. 'She must have pulled her lead from under the stool. One minute she was sitting here chewing her cud, and then she'd gone. I'm sorry, I don't know how she did it. Tom and Father have gone to look for her. I stayed with Pandora in case she tried to run off, too.'

'Oh no! Trust Berkeley! Don't worry, I'll go and look for her. She can't be far away. She's probably demolishing some of the plant stalls. Just stay with Pandora and hold on to her lead.'

I looked round, but there was no sign of the familiar black shape anywhere. She must have decided to follow me. I ran back towards the flower tent and the beer tent. There seemed to be people everywhere. Then I heard Berkeley's voice. She had seen me before I spotted her. She was walking towards me from the direction of the beer tent, being led by a tall, good-looking man, with a small boy on the other side of her. I ran up to them.

'Oh, you've found her, thank you so much. Wherever was she?'

The man smiled. He had dark hair and blue eyes that lingered on my face—inviting, caressing, like the gaze of a lover. There was something about him that I found interesting and at the same time disturbing.

'She was in the beer tent.' He was obviously amused. 'I

knew someone once who had a pet ram who liked a pint of beer. I wondered if she enjoyed one, too.'

'Did you give her one?'

He laughed. 'Sorry, no.'

'She's been really good all afternoon. I left them for a few minutes with my daughter and I suppose she wanted to follow me. I'm sorry if she's caused a lot of trouble.'

'Them? You mean there are more like her?'

'The other is a Jacob—an orphan lamb that I brought up on a bottle. I bought this one, Berkeley, as a weaned lamb to keep the other one company.'

'She's not doing her job, then?' He laughed again. I felt he was making fun of me as well as the sheep.

'I'm sorry,' I said again.

'Don't apologise. I like sheep. I've got some myself.'

'Oh, have you? What do you keep?'

'Mules, mostly; some Suffolks, a few Ryelands.'

'How many?'

'About five or six hundred.'

'A lot. I've got these two, that's all.'

'Want to borrow a ram in the autumn, then?'

'Well, no, not really, thank you. I wasn't going to breed from them. I just want them as pets. But I'd like some fleece. Do you have any Ryeland?'

'I did have. I keep the Ryeland back for spinners, but I sold the last two last week. You can certainly have some next year, though, if you want some. What are you doing here with two lambs? Spinning?'

'Yes. It's quite fun mostly, but it's surprising the things people say while they're watching. It's a nice way of meeting other people with similar interests, though.'

'My name's David Roberts. I'll give you my phone number. You might change your mind about a ram later on. Just give me a ring if you want any help.'

'Thank you, I will.' He still had hold of Berkeley's lead and we had nearly got back to Katy and Pandora. I hoped Gerald would not be there and, luckily, when we reached them Katy was on her own. Berkeley was fastened under the stool again. David Roberts picked up one of my cards and put it into his pocket, then wrote his name and address and telephone number on the back of a second card.

'Don't forget,' he said, handing it over.

'I won't, and thank you again for your help.'

'See you again some time,' he said, and then turned and walked back into the crowd, the small boy beside him.

'Well,' said Katy, 'who was that nice man, and where did he find Berkeley?'

'His name is David Roberts, and Berkeley was in the beer tent, would you believe. He grabbed her and was walking back with her when I met them. He's got sheep, too, about five hundred, he said. Quite useful to know in case I want some fleece or more bottle lambs.'

'He was very good-looking. He seemed to like you, too.' Katy was very perceptive. 'Where does he live?'

'Near Wetherbury. He's got a farm.'

'And a wife, too, I expect, Mother,' she said.

Just then Gerald and Tom came back and were most relieved to see Berkeley sitting down again, safely back in her place as if nothing had happened.

'Where did you find her?' asked Gerald.

'Just coming out of the beer tent,' I replied.

'Oh really, Berkeley,' scolded Gerald in mock severity. 'I hope she's not drunk.'

'Of course not. She wouldn't do anything like that. She just got bored and thought she'd have a look round.'

I returned to my spinning wheel but I found it hard to concentrate. My mind was with the tall, blue-eyed stranger. I had put the card with his name in my pocket. I wondered if I should see him again.

The following week I went to Castle Monkton to have coffee with Gerda, the Dutch lady I had met at the fête. Her husband, Ralph, was an elderly English writer, who had written some one hundred and fifty books. His latest, just published, was a life of Gainsborough. He was a darling old man in his eighties, with wispy white hair and faded blue eyes like old china. Gerda was some twenty years younger than he. She was short, with a round, happy face, and kindly smiling eyes. She had fair, close-cropped hair and was wearing a mulberry-coloured dress with embroidery round the hem. Ralph was wearing a jerkin which Gerda had made him from dark, handspun Hebridean wool. He had been reading a copy of *The Times*, but he put it to one side and stood up as Gerda showed me into their conservatory, which was full of scented-leaved geraniums, huge plants of Begonia Rex with red and green leaves, and enormous cactus with red and orange flowers.

They were so charming and welcoming. Gerda spoke perfect English, but slowly, almost shyly. Their house on the edge of the village was half hidden behind a tall brick wall. There was an archway in the wall and a green-painted wooden door which I had often noticed, but had had no idea what was to be found behind it.

Now, for the first time, I stepped through the doorway and found an almost enchanted world: a garden of old stone figures and giant ferns; mossy red-brick paths and urns tumbling with pink geraniums, cerastium and thunbergia; a summer jasmine with dark green leaves and sweetly scented white flowers climbed over the porch, meeting a cascade of Albertine roses on a massive plant which seemed to cover almost one wall of the house, twining round the upstairs windows until it nearly reached the steeply sloping roof.

The house was old, beamed and rambling with tiled floors and lovely wall hangings. One room—Ralph's study —was lined on every wall with books. Gerda and Ralph were so obviously happy in each other's company. They had been married for many years, but they looked at each other often and smiled. Gerda called him 'sweetheart' and would touch his arm while she was talking; I thought, almost sadly, how different my life with Gerald was. I was beginning more and more, to enjoy my days on my own and, after the weekend, found pleasure in the return of Monday and being alone again.

Gerda had made a special Dutch spice and apple cake for my visit, which was delicious. We ate it with coffee and then went out into the garden to the orchard at the back of the house. She had five white crossbred ewes in the

orchard, all with lambs at foot, and a small but cantanker-
ous Jacob ram. I remembered what Will had said and
thought he looked formidable indeed. He was four-horned,
like Pandora, but his horns were huge. The two top ones
were about eighteen inches long, sticking straight up out of
his skull; the side ones curled elegantly round his face.
Gerda was obviously wary of him. She showed me the door
to a garden shed, splintered as if by a madman with an axe,
and told me that 'Little Yeacoub had done that'.

I hoped fervently that 'Little Yeacoub' would keep his
horns to himself, but I need not have worried. He stalked
off to a corner of the orchard and began pulling crossly at
the grass. The ewes and lambs were sitting in a little group
under one of the apple trees, and we went and sat with
them. It was a hot summer's day and the trees made
dappled shadows on the grass as the sunlight filtered
through their leaves. The lambs got up and sniffed at us and
walked over Gerda's skirt. She sat stroking the head of one
of the ewes.

'She is a lovely old lady,' she said fondly, 'always such a
good mother. Ralph called her Ceres, the mother of all.'
Ceres, Goddess of plenty: taken from Greek Mythology as I
had taken my name for Pandora.

She told me that, like us, she and Ralph were vegetarians.

81

'I could not eat them,' she said, still stroking the old ewe's head. 'They are too beautiful.'

Her sheep seemed very gentle and well-behaved, and I thought of big, bold, pushing Berkeley, chewing holes in the hedge, trotting off up the lane, invading the beer tent and mugging visitors for biscuits. I was sure Gerda's sheep did not do things like that.

When we went back to the house Gerda showed me her spinning wheel and some of the things she had made. She had some wonderful jerseys, with intricate designs round the neck and yoke, made in several different natural colours of greys and browns. She said she never used patterns for her jerseys and knitted them always on circular needles. I was most impressed by them: they were certainly more unusual and attractive than any others I had ever seen. Gerda seemed surprised by my delight and enthusiasm. She had just made the jerseys for Ralph and herself and their children, now grown-up, but had not thought of them as anything more than functional garments to keep out the cold. They were truly works of art—each one individual and different.

Over the following months, as I got to know Gerda better, two of the endearing things I was to learn about her were her modesty and her complete lack of malice. I saw her happy, I saw her sad, but I never heard her say an unkind word about anyone.

I spent a very pleasant morning with her and her sheep and she promised to come and see my two again. As I drove home along the little lane between the cornfields, I thought what a happy coincidence it had been to meet Gerda at the school fête. We had been living within a few miles of each other and our interest in sheep had brought us together. I thought about David Roberts, the sheep farmer who lived near Wetherbury. Perhaps I should meet him again, too.

Chapter Six

The grass was now growing well in our meadow, and among it were already a number of wild flowers. Even the greedy Berkeley could not eat all of them. Two acres between her and Pandora was proving too much to decimate, even for her amazing appetite.

I went into their meadow one morning with a pencil and piece of paper to note how many different flowers there were. The barley field of the previous summer had looked well sprayed and weed-free, but many seeds must have been lying dormant in the soil, waiting for a chance to grow and blossom unheeded. Other seeds must have been brought by the birds. I had recently read an article in one of the Sunday newspapers about recolonisation of land by plants: it said that every year more varieties appeared and that if a meadow was left unsprayed there would be orchids growing in it after seven years. That seemed fairly unbelievable, given the scarcity of orchids generally, and I wondered how they could magically appear after seven years.

However, there were already a number of plants flowering in the meadow, appearing as if from nowhere. In the spring there had been cowslips beside the hedge and their clusters of leaves were still visible. At one side was a large clump of thistles which would be a haven for butterflies by autumn. I found beautiful white moon daisies; little field pansies, also known as heart's ease, the symbol of unrequited love; speedwells, black medick and scarlet pimpernel. As children we used to look for these little red flowers, to try and predict the weather—on fine days the flowers are open, but they close up at the hint of rain. There was chickweed, mayweed, fumitory and shepherd's purse, forget-me-not and ground ivy, and a large patch of corn mint making a sweetly scented carpet in a damp corner of the meadow near the hedge. I was surprised to find a few plants of centaury, with its bright pink flowers. It was a plant I associated with downland, which I had not found in Essex before. That was quite an exciting find.

There were flowers of red and white clover, too, but they had been in the grass seed mixture so they did not count. Perhaps the centaury had come in the same way. There were fat bumble bees on all the clover flowers and I hoped Berkeley would not inadvertently swallow one with a mouthful of lunch.

The hedge along one side of the meadow, with its great, spreading oak tree half-way along its length, gave welcome shade to Pandora and Berkeley now. When they had eaten as much as they could manage, they usually went and sat under the oak tree to chew their cud, instead of making their way down to the front doorsteps. The hen house had been moved from the back lawn to the field, near the gate and the old apple tree, and the hens spent their days wandering about with the sheep, pecking at the grass and clucking happily to themselves.

Having completed my flower count, I turned my attention to the hedge. It contained a large variety of trees and shrubs, including hornbeam. I knew that the age of a hedge could be roughly estimated by the number of different species in a thirty-yard stretch—one for approximately every hundred years. A hedge planted in Tudor times would have at least five different shrubs in it, and ten species could point to a hedge that might have originated in Saxon times. I was sure that the hedge was at least as old as our Tudor cottage, so I paced out roughly thirty yards from the oak tree and then walked back, writing down all the shrubs. There was ash to start, then a spindle bush, a crab-apple, hornbeam, hawthorn, wild cherry, more hawthorn, hazel, field maple, more hornbeam, elm, black-thorn, more field maple and hornbeam, holly and then finally the oak. That made twelve different species, not counting the dog rose and blackberry twining among the rest of the hedge. If the theory was correct the hedge was indeed very old.

It was a beautiful hedge. The owls called at night from the oak tree, greenfinches sang from the wild cherry branches. The berries from blackberries, hawthorn, blackthorn and holly fed the birds in winter, and the thick base of the hedge gave shelter to mice and voles. I found it reassuring to think of the hedge being there for perhaps a thousand years, giving food and shelter to birds and animals, in the same way that I found a comfort in our age-old house. It was more than just four walls: it had a presence, a spirit of its own.

At supper I told Gerald about the hedge, and he was quite intrigued. If it was really a thousand years old, it was reasonable to suppose that our Tudor cottage had been built on the site of an even earlier dwelling.

By the end of July the cornfields each side of our cottage were golden. The ripe ears of wheat bent downwards ready for harvesting, and sparrows descended on them in noisy little groups. The sky was clear, bright blue, the roadsides dusty, and the trees and hedges looking ragged and insect-torn. There were large clumps of white daisy-flowered mayweed in the field gateway next to the lane, and the clay soil there had dried and was covered in deep cracks, looking like rivers on a map.

The children were now home from school for the summer holidays. Katy bundled her hated school uniform into her wardrobe and dressed herself in pale blue jeans and shirts of thin Indian cotton and her dolls'-slipper shoes. The strands of hair at the back of her neck were now permanently adorned with beads and she usually spent half an hour every morning plaiting them into her dark hair with different-coloured ribbons.

Tom's school tie had a very mysterious way of disappearing with unfailing regularity during term-time, but was now officially abandoned.

He and Alex spent the long, hot days in the meadow or

garden—cleaning out the chicken house, sitting in the tree house or making expeditions across to the wood.

They put up a tent at the top of the meadow and built a camp fire, making a double circle of bricks and collecting dry leaves and twigs from the hedge. They finally managed to get it going, and thick drifts of smoke began to creep across the grass. Berkeley was very interested in the tent: she stuck her head through the flap and tried to get inside.

Tom and Alex shooed her away and she finally retreated, more from the smoke than their arm-waving. They scurried about, finding more fuel for the fire, and Alex was sent to the house for provisions. He trudged backwards and forwards between the top of the meadow and the house, carrying sleeping bags and food, a saucepan and a container of water. The smoke lessened and finally they had quite a good fire.

Katy and I sat under the oak tree. Katy had her sketch book and paints with her and was drawing the view across to the blue hills. I had my bag of wools and my crochet hook, making more shawls for the shop in Chelsea.

Gerald came home, and when he had changed out of his suit we took mugs of tea on a tray into the meadow and sat on the grassy bank near the gate.

'This is like being in another world,' Gerald said, looking across the cornfields and rubbing Berkeley's black head between her ears. 'When I am shut inside all day with my books I like to think of you here, but this place seems so far removed from everywhere else it could be a hundred miles away.'

He poured some of his tea onto the tray for Berkeley, and after she had gobbled up a couple of digestive biscuits she turned her attention to the tea. It was soon gone, and then she licked the tray all over with her fat black tongue.

'Did you enjoy that, Berkeley?' he asked.

Her answer was to scrape at his leg with one of her front feet.

'She wants some more,' said Katy, laughing. 'You'll have to give her the rest of your tea.'

'The boys want you to inspect their camp,' I said to

Gerald. 'They've made a really good fire and they're busy cooking at the moment.'

'Very well,' and he began walking up the meadow. Katy and I and the lambs followed him. Tom and Alex were sitting near their fire, eating a potato each that they had wrapped in foil and cooked in the hot ashes. The potatoes had taken most of the afternoon to cook but were obviously worth waiting for. Some beans were now heating up in the saucepan.

'We're going to have pizza and salad for supper,' I said. 'Do you want any?'

'Yes, please,' they said together, 'but no salad, thanks,' added Tom.

I took theirs up to them first. Pandora and Berkeley were wandering about in the middle of the meadow nibbling at the clover. After her initial interest, Berkeley had not been near the camp fire again.

We took our supper into the field and sat on the grass near the hedge. The air was warm under the trees. Swallows were flying round the garden and low over the meadow; the two that had made their nest in the barn now had four youngsters with them, darting after little insects as gracefully and carelessly as their parents, only distinguished by their shorter tails.

'I hope the weather stays like this next week,' said Gerald. 'What do you want to do?' He would be on holiday and had decided against the ruins of Rome in favour of the peace and quiet of Monk's Green.

Before I could answer, there were happy shouts from the middle of the field and Pandora and Berkeley came running towards us. Pandora reached us first and stood looking at us with her head on one side, then Berkeley trotted up, licking her black lips. Food always seemed to be uppermost in her mind.

'Watch your supper,' I said as she nosed around, eyeing the plates. She trotted round us and Gerald waved his arm at her. She began nibbling at the clover flowers.

'Let's go to the sea,' said Katy, 'can we? With Uncle Rodney and Auntie Melissa?'

She and Gerald loved the sea. The coast was not some-where I would choose to go on my own—there always seemed to be a chill breeze on the hottest day—but I liked the trips we made to Dunwich. The sandy Suffolk roadsides were lined with fennel, and weld grew in profusion on the rough heathland around Dunwich. I always came back with armfuls of both to dye my wool. Rodney and Melissa were renting a cottage for two months, in the little Suffolk village of Ickling Green, and we could collect them on the way.

'I'd like to go to Wicken Fen,' I said, 'and Ely.' I had not been to Wicken for years, but as a child it had been one of my favourite places. I remembered the black Fenland peat soil, and the dykes full of flowering rush and water-soldier. Rodney and I had spent hours there look-ing for swallowtail butterflies. It was supposed to be the last remaining habitat in England for this beautiful butterfly, and although we never saw any, we did not doubt that they were there. We should see them next time.

I had invited Ralph and Gerda to come and have lunch. It was another beautiful, cloudless day and we decided to eat in the garden. Katy helped me mix the salads and get the food ready, and we left it covered over in the pantry. They arrived smiling and happy, and Gerda brought me a bunch of flowers from their garden—scabious, asters, daisies and sweet-scented verbena.

Ralph sat in the shade at the back of the house reading the *Guardian*, while Gerda and I went to talk to the lambs. We took some biscuits for them and they came running towards us, Pandora's tail swinging as she ran.

'Hello, little ones,' said Gerda, stroking their noses, 'do you want some food?' and she held out the biscuits to them. Pandora nibbled at hers, taking small bites off it and eating each one separately, but Berkeley tried to cram all the biscuit into her mouth at once.

'My, but you are a greedy one,' said Gerda.

'She is awful, she eats everything. She nearly killed herself with half a sack of chicken food. She ate through the telephone wire and cut us off. She's had all the roses and the raspberry canes.'

Gerda laughed and stroked Pandora's face. 'She is gentle, this one, but she has horns like "Little Yeacoub". Will they grow very large?'

'I do hope not. I don't think she'll have any at the side now. She did have two little ones each side of her head, but she kept knocking them on things and they were always bleeding. Now they are just two small lumps. The vet says they won't grow any more as she is a ewe, although rams grow their horns again if they break. So she is a four-horn Jacob with only two horns.'

The hens were clucking and scratching about in the grass near us. They now had red-gold feathers and bright combs—I had almost forgotten how pathetic they had been when Gerald had first brought them home.

'We used to have some chickens—bantams,' said Gerda. 'The mother hen would go off and make a nest in the hedge somewhere, and then one day she would come out leading all these fluffy little chicks. I loved to see them. I miss the bantams, but there is enough to do now with the sheep. We are not so young as we used to be,' she added a little wistfully.

We wandered idly about in the meadow, followed by Pandora and Berkeley, and Gerda talked about all the sheep she had had over the years. When we went back to the garden, Ralph looked up from the paper and smiled.

'Oh, sweetheart, they are such fun, Lizzy's lambs, but so greedy,' said Gerda laughing.

Katy and I carried out the lunch and set it on the table on the back lawn. Ralph told us over lunch that their house had been built on the site of a Roman villa. When he had first moved there thirty years ago, he had uncovered a brick and tile floor, some of it still in good condition. He had found a lot of broken pottery, oyster shell and charred bones. He had made a proper dig over two summers, going down to three feet and marking the levels as he went. The grass had grown over the Roman floor, but it was still there below the surface, and the finds from the dig were in carefully labelled boxes. A few of his finds had gone to the County town museum, but most he still had at home.

'How exciting. Gerald would love to see them, he's mad on archaeology. He's always going off on digs at weekends. He was talking about doing a dig in the corner of the garden this summer. There must be a lot of bits and pieces scattered about in the garden, and probably this house is built on the site of an earlier one.'

'You must bring Gerald to see us,' said Gerda.

There were some rustling sounds in the hedge at the back of the lawn and a black face appeared. Berkeley saw the plates and glasses and the food on the table. She started pushing. Earlier in the summer, when she had been in the garden, she had been constantly pushing or eating her way through this hedge to get into the meadow. Now she was in the meadow she wanted to be back in the garden.

'Go back, Berkeley,' I said to her, getting up and walking towards her. As I reached her she broke through the hedge and trotted across the lawn. Pandora followed and, before I could grab them, they had reached the table and started helping themselves.

'Oh, my goodness,' cried Gerda, 'you are naughty sheep. Go away, you can't have our food.'

I took hold of Berkeley's collar and pulled her away from the table, while Katy held Pandora. They were marched off to the barn and shut in their pen.

'Oh, I am sorry! How awful they are!' I viewed the table in dismay. They had knocked over the glasses, and scattered what was left of our salad. Luckily we had just about finished eating when they appeared.

But Gerda was laughing. 'Don't worry about it,' she said. 'We had finished anyway.' Katy and I took the remains inside and I made some coffee.

'It isn't every day, after all, that we have lunch with some sheep,' said Ralph.

When they left Gerda hugged me.

'Thank you, we have had a lovely day. Do bring Gerald to see us, won't you? I am so glad I have met you.'

I was glad that I had met her, too. She and Ralph were two of the kindest, most charming people I knew.

Ickling Green, where Rodney and Melissa had their cottage, had one main street lined with rows of little flint cottages. Some had roses round their doors and house martins flying up to the eaves. The front door of number six was wide open, and as we stopped outside Melissa appeared, smiling and sun-tanned in a pale blue cotton dress, the colour of her eyes. She was carrying a large picnic basket. Rodney came out after her, a denim jacket slung over his shoulder, ducking his head as he stepped out onto the path, and locked the door behind him. The basket was stowed into the boot and Rodney sat in front with Gerald while Melissa and I sat in the back with the children. Gerald's two-litre car was large and ate up the miles with satisfying speed; we were soon within a few miles of the sea.

'Ten pence for whoever sees the sea first,' said Rodney.

'Well, I can smell it,' I said, winding down the car window and breathing in the fresh, salty air.

'I can see it,' said Tom excitedly.

'So can I,' said Katy.

'Right, you both get ten pence, then, and I'll race you down the beach,' said Rodney. 'Last one in the sea's a dunce.'

There was a mad scramble out of the car when we stopped. Rodney and the children went running down the shingle, shouting and laughing. Melissa and I spread the picnic cloth and unpacked the food.

Gerald unfolded the rug and stretched himself out on it in the sun, to soak up its heat. He had taken off his shirt and lay, eyes closed, on his back, wearing a pair of fawn coloured shorts and his socks and shoes. I had noticed before how loath men always seem to take off their socks and shoes, and always found it vaguely ridiculous. I removed my shoes at every opportunity, and had once spent a hot summer evening walking around London barefoot, much to the horror of my male companion.

Melissa and I discarded our sandals and I pushed my toes idly into the warm pebbles.

'Oh, I'm so hungry now,' I said. 'It must be the sea air. You've brought such a lot—it looks lovely.'

Melissa had made rolls with salad in, and little pinto bean and buckwheat pies. There were hard-boiled eggs and individual cheeses wrapped in red foil, and a tin full of her home-made American cookies.

'Rodney put in the elderflower wine, but he's got the opener in his pocket,' she said. 'We made it this spring, when we were still at Bracknell.'

We sat on the rug and watched Rodney and the children running about at the water's edge. Tom had found some pieces of seaweed and he was throwing it at the other two.

'I shall miss you two such a lot,' I said. 'So will the children.'

'I know,' said Melissa, 'and we're going to miss you. It's just that with Rodney's job he doesn't have too many options. He couldn't stand living in London, but working there and living in Suffolk would mean four hours' travelling time every day. The only other place in the UK he can work is Aberdeen, and he's been up there for a spell as you know. He says it's so cold and it always rains. He loves the sun, that's what he likes so much about Texas. You must come and visit. We thought maybe the kids could come next summer in their long vacation, if you and Gerald wouldn't mind.'

'That would be wonderful for them. They'd love it.'

Rodney and the children came back then and collapsed on the rug, tired and hot from their exertions. Rodney opened the wine.

'Who's driving?' he said, looking at Gerald and handing him a glass. 'That means more for the rest of us. Cheers!'

Melissa's pies were delicious and we greedily ate nearly all the food, leaving a few cookies in the tin for later. We packed up the basket and Rodney volunteered to take it to the car. He returned holding a book.

'Present for you kids,' he said to Tom and Katy. It was called *The Pebbles on the Beach*.

'Oh, thank you, Uncle Rodney, how lovely,' said Katy.

'Gosh, thanks,' said Tom.

Katy turned the pages to look at the coloured illustrations with their keys to identification.

'Can we go and collect some stones now? Will you come with us and help us find some amber?'

'I don't know if we'll find any amber,' said Rodney, 'but I'll help you look. We can find lots of other different stones, though.'

We all started walking along the beach, Katy and Gerald slowly, peering at the stones, Tom running about still waving his piece of seaweed.

The sun was hot and I could feel it burning through the thin cotton of my Indian blouse in spite of the faint breeze from the sea. I walked along by the edge of the water, my bare feet sinking into the smooth sand, the hem of my long cotton skirt soaked by the waves lapping in and out, making rivulets in the sand and sparkling the pebbles. I picked up a piece of driftwood and scratched idly in the sand.

'Hi, Sis!' called Rodney. 'What are you doing?'

'Trying to think of something profound to write in the sand.'

'Did you say profane?'

'No . . . profound.'

'What about "Life is a four-letter word"?' said Rodney. 'Or "Obesity kills"? That's a good one for Berkeley. Pass it on to her.'

We started laughing and sat on the pebbles drawing patterns in the sand. Tom and Katy joined us.

'Let's have a competition,' said Rodney, 'to see who can draw the best giant rat,' and he began scratching with the driftwood. Tom started drawing a line along the beach.

'Where are you going, Tom?' called his uncle.

'You said a giant rat, so he's going to be huge. This is his tail.'

'He'll stretch from here to Aldeburgh, then, I should think.'

We fell about laughing. Luckily the beach was almost deserted. The sun and the wine had made us silly.

'Come on, Uncle Rodney, help us find some amber, please,' said Katy bored with drawing rats.

We got up and walked along the shingle. I picked up some tiger stones, black-banded agates that looked like ewes' eyes, and I found a wishing stone—a stone with a hole worn through its centre by the steady flow of the sea. I held it up and saw the blue sky through its heart.

We stopped on the heathland on the way home and picked bunches of heather, and I gathered weld and fennel for my wool. When we got to the little cottage at Ickling Green Melissa and I made a cup of tea, while Rodney and the children spread out the stones they had picked up and matched them with pictures in the book. Rodney's love of geology made visits to the seaside more fun, and Tom and Katy spent a happy half-hour sorting through the stones with him. They had not found any amber, but they had a small piece of red cornelian. They had agates and onyx, quartzite and citrine, and Katy had a bag of tiny pink and white shells.

We finally arrived home at Monk's Green, tired and sunburned but happy after our day. As we drove along the lane I saw Pandora and Berkeley half-way up the meadow behind the cottage. They heard the car and looked up, then started running, and as we turned in at the gateway they were there to meet us.

I tied the fennel and weld in bunches and hung them on the back wall of the cottage to dry. They would yield colour equally well dried and I should be able to save them for winter use when there were few plants growing outside. I put the stones in a little earthenware pot on the dresser, and every morning I picked up the wishing stone and turned it over in my hand.

We spent some afternoons along the lane digging for roots of bedstraw. The tiny clouds of yellow or white flowers were everywhere. The roots were long and stringy, but they made the most wonderful pink and red dyes when boiled with the wool. Bedstraw is a close relative of madder, grown on the continent for the dyes madder-red, madder-brown and rose madder.

We also went on what was always referred to afterwards as 'The Great Woad Hunt'.

My sister Meg came to stay for a few days. Her children were in France with their father, a rather eccentric musician, whom she had divorced some years ago. Meg was younger than I, with hazel eyes and lovely red-gold hair that I had always envied as a child.

She could not understand my passion for animals but tolerated it good-humouredly. She loathed dogs, especially my noisy trio, and they always seemed naughtier whenever she came to see us. She was amused by the sheep. They were quite ridiculous, she said, with such fat bodies and skinny legs, but she was surprised how friendly and affectionate they were.

Cats, however, she loved. She had two herself that she had had as kittens. They had been found one winter by the local cat shelter, nearly starved to death, and Meg had taken them in. They had been wild, terrified little bundles of fur that had spat and screamed when she tried to pick them up, but gradually they had calmed and got used to their new surroundings. Now, years later, as fat, lazy, black and white cats, usually asleep in the middle of her bed, it was hard to believe that they had ever been such pathetic kittens.

Meg approved of our cats, and I told her how they had come to us as strays when we had moved into the cottage.

'They're lovely,' she said, sitting on the front door steps in the sun, while they rubbed around her, waving their tails in the air. 'Which is which? That's Ursula, is it, the brown one? Which one is Barrington?'

They were all pointed out to her, especially Barrington, who had been so scraggy and mangy when we had first taken her in. She was now twice the size, with long, soft, brown tabby fur.

'I thought she was a tom when I called her Barrington,' I said. 'I suppose I should change it, but we've got used to calling her that.'

96

'Oh, I think it's rather fun,' she said, 'like Carrington, you know.'

Yes, like Lytton Strachey's Carrington. At least it was different. There couldn't be many female tabbies about with a name like that. So Barrington she remained.

Over supper that evening we discussed what we were going to do the next day. I suggested a trip to Tewkesbury. They looked at me in surprise.

'Why Tewkesbury?' asked Gerald. 'It's rather a long way.'

'Famous for its mustard,' said Meg.

'I want to go and look for some woad. It grows all over the cliffs there, about the only place to find it growing wild. Anyway, it's not that far, only about a hundred and fifty miles. I thought it would be fun to go, just for the day. It's near Worcester and all those lovely places in the Cotswolds. And I want some woad to try dyeing my wool blue.'

'Can't you get some plants from a nursery?' asked Gerald. 'It would be much easier.'

Katy and Meg, however, were all in favour of a day trip to Tewkesbury. Meg was not fond of driving but was a very willing passenger, and I loved it. Tom did not want to be sitting in the car all day—he and Alex had other plans —and Gerald preferred to stay and look after the animals, so Katy, Meg and I would have a day out together.

We left early the next morning, just before six o'clock. After reaching Wetherbury, we turned onto the long, un-dulating roads that ran the rolling hills on the Hertfordshire border. Soon we reached the little thatched, red-brick cottages of Bedfordshire, and then the wide-open spaces of the Cotswolds, the houses built of the beautiful yellow-grey stone. We had Gerald's car and it accelerated with ease along the smooth, open roads.

We stopped in Chipping Norton. The tall stone houses and wide, sunlit streets were so different from the little thatch and plaster cottages and narrow lanes we had left behind. We went into a craft shop for coffee. Katy and I had a large cream cake each, but Meg sat and smoked a cigarette with her coffee and watched us disapprovingly.

'I don't know why you don't get fat,' she said to me. 'You're always eating cakes.'

I had to admit that Katy and I usually rated towns and villages by the number of pre-twentieth century houses to be found and the excellence or otherwise of their bakeries.

We drove on towards Stow-on-the-Wold, by-passing a village called Adlestrop.

'So this is Adlestrop—' said Meg.

'Was—' I said as we flashed past the sign.

'But you must have heard of it—' and she began reciting a poem immortalising the railway line through Adlestrop. I was ashamed to admit I had never heard of the poem, nor indeed the place, but Meg was far more well-read than I. I stopped the car and turned in a gateway and drove back round the village. It was small and quiet, with little stone cottages lining the main street. We saw the famous station with its large black and white sign—about all that was left of its railwaying days—but Meg was delighted.

'That poem,' she mused, 'I've read it so many times, and now I've actually been here.'

We drove on and reached Tewkesbury soon after noon. There were some beautiful half-timbered black and white houses but no sign of the cliffs.

'Let's have lunch first,' I said, 'and then get the woad afterwards.'

We went to one of the old inns and sat in a little brick courtyard at the back, among tubs of geraniums and petunias. As I sipped my gin and tonic, I looked at all the old roofs, different shapes and pitches, fitting into and against each other at the backs of the houses. They had tiny mossy tiles, some covered with stonecrop and houseleek, and above them was the enormous tower of the church— Tewkesbury Abbey as it had been before the Dissolution.

'Which way are the cliffs?' asked Meg. 'Will there be a sign, "To the Woad"?'

'I don't know where they are. I thought we'd just see them when we got here.' I had pictured them standing out above the town, covered with the small yellow flowers and dark green rosettes of next year's plants. Perhaps other woad hunters would be there, too. Meg thought it very unlikely.

When we had finished lunch we went back to the car.

'They must be next to the river, so if we find that first, perhaps we'll find the cliffs.' We had a choice of roads: 'Which way, Gloucester or Worcester?'

'You choose,' she said.

I chose Worcester, because I liked it better, and it was on the edge of the Malvern hills. I was tempted to forget the woad and go and sit on Bromyard Downs and look at the sheep. We crossed the river by a wide, modern bridge and found the road climbing steeply. I stopped at the top of the hill. The town was below us with the wide river Severn flowing between flat green fields and wooded banks.

'I think we've found the cliffs,' said Katy. 'It must be this, it's the only hill.'

I turned the car and headed back towards the bridge. Near the bridge was a gravelled lay-by and a sign pointing to a public footpath, so I pulled in and stopped the car.

We set out along the footpath, through copse-like under-growth of scrubby elders and brambles, interspersed with stinging nettles. We turned a corner and found ourselves on a grassy path next to the river. There were clouds of little gnats and water forget-me-nots at its edge. We walked on and then suddenly, without warning, on our side of the river the ground rose up in great orange-coloured cliffs—steep, bare slopes of red sandstone. All eyes were now on the cliffs, looking for the elusive woad. Suddenly I saw one small plant about thirty feet above us.

'There's one!' I cried. 'Look, there must be more. At least we've found the right place.'

'Is that woad?' said Katy, greatly disappointed. 'You mean we've come all this way to look at that?'

Meg laughed loudly. 'That is woad,' she said. 'Take a long look, because I think it's the only piece you're going to see.'

'Well, I know it looks a bit dull,' I said, 'but it's a very interesting plant. The Ancient Britons got their dye from it and it used to grow wild everywhere. We'll find some more

in a minute and I'll collect some seeds to grow in the garden.'

We walked on past a bare wall of sandstone. Then I saw a second plant about as inaccessible as the first.

'I'm going to climb up and get some seeds,' I said.

'Don't be an idiot,' said Meg, 'you can't get up there. You'll fall if you try, and break your ankle. If you don't go in the river and drown,' she added.

I tried to scramble up, the loose earth slipping under my feet. I managed to get to the plant eventually and saw several small, dark rosettes of green growing next to it. They would be plants to flower next year, as woad is a biennial, flowering in its second year, the plant then dying after setting seed. I had not imagined the plant would be so scarce here, so it seemed a sin to take any seeds. But I picked two off and put them in my pocket.

I turned to climb down. The red sandstone seemed like a straight wall to the ground, the river bank very near the bottom. I leaned back, my foot wedged on a piece of rock.

'I think I'm stuck,' I said to them.

Meg was sitting on the river bank watching me with a mixture of anxiety and amusement.

'Your mother's crazy,' she said to Katy, as she puffed a cigarette and contemplated my predicament.

Katy was very agitated. 'You'll fall, Mother,' she said, 'do be careful.'

I slid down somehow, covering my skirt with dust and my legs with scratches and bruises.

'Where to next?' asked Meg.

'We'll go to Wales for tea, and then we'll go home.'

We drove on towards Worcester and then over the downs and to the border of Wales. There were the beautiful dark hills covered with sheep. I felt elated by the afternoon. The thought that later we would have to drive back again, a distance of some two hundred miles, was unimportant now. We found a little village shop that sold Welsh teas and we had a pot of tea and steaming hot Welsh cakes covered with butter.

I bought a postcard for Tom with a red Welsh dragon on it, and wrote it while I had my tea. As we left I put it in the post box outside.

'But he won't have it until after you're back,' said Meg.

'Never mind, the idea's fun,' I answered, 'and it will have a Welsh postmark.'

We drove back through Worcester and the Vale of Evesham, stopping to buy some baskets of plums. I would make mine into jam to eat during the winter as a reminder of our day out, and Meg was going to make hers into wine.

'I have enjoyed it,' she said. 'It's made a lovely change. You're quite mad, but I'm glad I came.'

'Let's do it again. Only next time we'll miss out Tewkesbury and have lunch in Ledbury. Then we can have all afternoon in Wales.'

'All right,' she agreed, 'as long as you drive.'

I planted the woad seeds in the garden. Perhaps one day I should have some plants.

Chapter Seven

And then the long summer holidays were over. The days were still hot at noon, but the mornings were damp, misty, covered with dew, and the evening air smelled of woodsmoke and toadstools. Now the pale flowers of summer were gone from the roadsides, and in their place were tall russet spikes of sorrel, clumps of grey-green mugwort and bright yellow flowers of ragwort, their leaves tattered and chewed to threads by the striped orange caterpillars of the cinnabar moth.

The autumn air always seemed so still and perfect. The warm soft breeze of summer had gone, the icy winds of winter were yet to come, and in between was the peace of autumn, like time standing still.

I let Pandora and Berkeley out of the barn and they made their way to the meadow and, once inside the gate, put their heads down into their bowls of nuts. The hens came flapping and squawking out of their house, eager for their breakfast. The grass in the meadow was still damp. There were little clusters of pale toadstools in the long grass under the hedge. The leaves were already beginning to drop and make a carpet of brown and yellow.

A group of starlings were sitting in the top of one of the willows and I listened to them whistling and chuckling among the green and yellow leaves, their plumage brightly iridescent in the clear September sun. A line of swallows was twittering on the telegraph wires in the lane, red cheeks and blue-black wings glistening. Soon they would be gone on their terrible journey. It never failed to amaze me that they could travel such distances. Many of them died, I knew, and it always seemed such a dreadful waste to me; but somehow the swallows came back every spring: some of them survived the marathon journey. Every so often they swooped down from the wires, flying in low circles across the garden and then back to their perch. I wondered which of them were the two who had nested in the barn and hoped they would find their way back again next year.

'Come back safely, little birds,' I whispered as I watched them.

Rodney and Melissa, too, would soon be going away on their long journey, flying many thousands of miles over the sea like the swallows, but they would not be back next spring and I would miss them greatly.

They came over later that morning and we sat outside the open cottage doorway in the warm, still day, drinking coffee. Then Rodney went to the meadow to inspect Pandora and Berkeley. They had heard Rodney's car and were standing by their gate looking hopefully for biscuits.

'My God, Berkeley's enormous. And what a ridiculous shape. Is she meant to be as fat as that?'

'A lot of it is wool,' I said, 'but she is rather huge. She's so greedy, that's the trouble, she's always eating.'

She gave some hopeful bleats, showing her black tongue.

'Berkeley-burgers on the hoof,' said Rodney laughing.

She pushed up to us, nosing about, nibbling at the pockets on my skirt. Pandora put her head on one side and looked inquisitively at Rodney. He produced some biscuit for them and Berkeley ate greedily, gobbling her pieces so quickly that she had twice as much as Pandora. Melissa had followed us to the gate.

'They are so cute,' she said, coming into the field. 'Pandora is so much bigger and her wool has got so long.' She ran her hand down the side of Pandora's neck. 'It's really soft, and such pretty colours. I've never seen a sheep like her before. Just wait till I tell all the folks back in Texas about you, Pandora. And about Berkeley—but my goodness, she's so big. They're not still lambs, are they? Surely they must be sheep by now.'

103

'They're lambs until the end of the year that they're born. On January 1st they'll stop being lambs and become hoggets, and then when they're sheared next summer they'll be sheep.'

'Hoggets,' mused Melissa, 'that's a strange name for sheep. It sounds like it should belong to hogs.'

Pigs were always hogs to Melissa, like the old English. Our medieval house in the village, from which we had moved to live here, was shown as having a 'hogs cote' in the garden on an eighteenth-century map we had found—the old name for pigsty.

When the biscuits were finished we walked up the field and Pandora and Berkeley followed us. Rodney made his way across to a huge clump of thistles, a mass of purple flowers, thistledown and butterflies. I have to admit to being rather fond of thistles. The flowers had a sweet scent, and the children and I had spent many happy hours on our country walks, when they were young, collecting bags of thistledown to use for stuffing cushions and pillows for Katy's dolls' house. Tom and Katy had long outgrown making dolls' cushions, or chairs and tables from conkers and pins wound with wool, but whenever I saw a mass of soft thistledown I always wanted to gather it into a bag for later use.

Rodney was inspecting the butterflies. His hobby was entomology and he had an impressive collection. There were dozens of little tawny skippers and several small tortoiseshells and some beautiful Peacock butterflies. I did not have Rodney's scientific, analytical interest in them, but I loved them for their fragile beauty and their representation of peace and warmth. I could not imagine a summer without butterflies, any more than I could imagine a world without birds.

At one time I had thought that caterpillars would eat anything, but Rodney had taught me that each species had a specific food plant and I was beginning to learn some of them, so that now I knew that the stinging nettles behind the barn, which I cursed earlier in the year when chasing Pandora and Berkeley, had fed the caterpillars that had become these lovely small tortoiseshell and Peacock butter-flies, and that the skippers had started life as smooth green caterpillars feeding on grass stems.

We had lunch inside, at the pine kitchen table, just in case of ovine invasion. We ate salads and cheese and French bread, and Rodney and Melissa had brought some blackberry wine which they had made the previous autumn. It was rich and smooth, and a wonderful deep red colour.

'Here's to your new life,' I said, holding out my glass.

Rodney and Melissa raised their glasses and touched mine. 'And here's to you and your sheep,' said Rodney.

We drank in silence for a few moments. I still could not believe that they were really going, and I wanted to beg Rodney not to leave England, not to go so far away. I sensed a sudden reluctance in him, and I knew that if I had tried hard enough to persuade him to stay when he had first spoken about living in America, he would not be going now. But that would have been unfair, and now it was all too late. Their flights were booked for two weeks' time, their house was sold and most of their furniture was already half-way across the Atlantic. I looked at Rodney sitting opposite me, trying to remember every detail of his face, burning the picture into my mind for when he was no longer there—the strong, angular, determined line of his jaw, the way his mouth turned up slightly at the corners, so that he always looked happy, the smiling blue eyes, the fair hair, with the reddish tinge to it when the sunlight caught it. I had a sudden panic feeling that I might never see him again. I felt the tears behind my eyes, so I said nothing and finished my wine quickly. Rodney laughed and refilled my glass.

'You'll be drunk in charge of a sheep,' he said. 'I wonder if that's an offence. Being drunk in charge of a horse is . . . Probably, just drunk and disorderly would do.'

Melissa laughed then, too. She had a lovely face and her eyes sparkled when she was happy. She at least would be looking forward to their move. To her it would be going home to the land where she belonged, where she had been born.

'The wine is good,' she said, 'it's the first bottle we opened. We were saving it for a special occasion. You should make some this year and then when we come back to visit we can sample it.'

Rodney had brought a dozen bottles of blackberry with them and some bottles of gooseberry wine that they had made a couple of months earlier and which needed maturing. He put them at the back of the pantry with 'do not open until next year' labels on them.

He opened another bottle of blackberry and we all cheered up. He started telling us about his escapades at boarding school and had Melissa and me in fits of laughter.

Rodney then decided we were going to make an expedition along the lane to gather blackberries, naturally taking Pandora and Berkeley with us.

'They like going "tenting",' I said, taking the leads off the back of the kitchen door.

'I beg your pardon,' said Rodney, 'I know Berkeley is very adaptable, but I had not envisaged spending the night with her under canvas.'

'No, "tenting" is an old English word—it means taking them for a walk so they can graze at the same time. Just letting them amble along, nibbling as they go. It's what people used to do, and they'd probably knit as they walked.'

'Why not? What a great idea. Where are the old knitting needles, then?'

I found some bowls from the cupboard. 'We're getting blackberries today—remember?'

We went to the gate into the field and I called to the sheep. Pandora and Berkeley came running down towards me with happy shouts of recognition, Pandora's tail swinging as she skipped and jumped through the clover. Berkeley did some ridiculous jumps—all four feet a few inches off the ground at once—bumping woodenly towards us like a child running a sack race.

Rodney laughed so much he nearly fell over.

'Oh, God, you have some crazy sheep.'

We fastened the leads on and Rodney took hold of Berkeley, who had come to an abrupt halt and was now looking decidedly breathless, her fat black sides heaving in and out. As soon as the gate was opened she lurched forward, dragging Rodney with her, and took several large mouthfuls out of the hedge.

We got them into the lane. Melissa declined the offer of Pandora's lead although she was always good and well behaved, so I took Pandora and Melissa carried the bowls. There were plenty of blackberries along the lane. The sheep stopped often, so I held both leads and sat in the grass while Rodney and Melissa gathered the fruit.

Some of the fields had been ploughed and were brown instead of yellow. There were plenty of hazel bushes in the hedge, with clusters of ripening nuts. The hedge was quite tall and they were out of reach of me and Melissa, but Rodney reached up and picked some and stuffed them into his pocket. While he was picking them he found a soft grassy nest, half-way up the hedge, and called us excitedly to look at it. It was a dormouse's nest—something I had never seen before.

The leaves on the hedge were still mostly green, but here and there some elm leaves were turning yellow, and the dogwood leaves already had a reddish tinge. The grass beside the lane was full of vetches—yellow vetching and bird's foot trefoil and the pale pink pea-like flowers of restharrow; great spreading purple tangles of bush vetch. In the hedge were the strange drooping flowers of woody nightshade, and already some scarlet berries. There were purple knobbly heads of knapweed, feathery grasses and drying seedheads of cow parsley and hogweed.

A flock of rosy-breasted pigeons was walking about in a field of barley stubble and, as we drew near them, they rose up in a great cloud and clattered away, making a half-circle towards the farm and then coming to rest in the field beyond.

'I shall miss all this very much,' said Rodney. 'I've always loved the autumn, and going blackberrying. Don't forget to

107

write and tell me all you're doing, about the sheep and the cottage and the kids, and just country walks like this.'

As well as blackberry-picking time, autumn was also sheep-dipping time. I had been dreading this, throwing my poor lambs into the cold evil-smelling bath.

Ian phoned one morning and said that he would be dipping his the next day and I could take mine up there to put in his sheep dip.

'I suppose they should be done . . .'

'It discourages the flies for one thing, but the main reason they're dipped is to stop sheep scab,' said Ian. 'Have you seen what scab does to a sheep?'

'No.'

'Well, if you had, you'd want them dipped. It's a mite that gets under the skin and causes them intense irritation. They rub and rub themselves until they rub all their wool off, and their skin, sometimes.'

'What time should we come?'

'It doesn't matter. You can come in the evening when Gerald gets home, if you like. I'll cover the dip over instead of draining it, and they can go in when you bring them. Don't worry, it won't hurt them. I always throw the sheep dogs in, too; it gets rid of their fleas.'

The next evening, when Gerald came home, we spread sheets of polythene in the car and loaded Pandora and Berkeley up for the trip to Ian's farm.

The dip was set into concrete, surrounded by hurdles and pens to run the sheep down and into the dip, and then let them stand and drain afterwards before being turned back to their grazing. Ian's sheep were all back in their fields and the yard at the back of the barns was empty.

Ian came out of the farmhouse as we drove up, and we unloaded Pandora and Berkeley and I led them up to the pens. I took their collars and leads off and Ian grabbed hold of Pandora and, turning her half onto her side, pushed her into the dip bath. Berkeley made to run off, but he grabbed her, too, and threw her in with Pandora. She gasped as she hit the cold water. They struggled and swam round frantically, striking out with their front legs to try and find

108

something on which to clamber out. Pandora shouted loudly for help, looking at me with terrified eyes, probably thinking she was drowning. Ian put his boot on her head and pushed it under, and when she bobbed up again she called out with desperation in her voice.

She was shouting to me for help and I did nothing.

'They must think they're going to drown,' I said miserably. It was awful. But I had to stand and watch and wait for it to end.

'Nonsense,' said Ian, 'don't fuss. They're perfectly all right. Spoilt, that's all.'

At last Ian turned them round so that their hooves touched the ramp, and they scrambled out, dripping like sea monsters. Pandora looked at me sadly, her eyes reddened by the dip, and bleated again. She shivered and I heard her teeth chatter. Then she shook herself like a dog, filling the air with a thousand rainbowed drops, shaking her body dry and then her head, separately. Berkeley shook herself, too, and then, before I could fasten their collars back on, they ran as fast as they could towards the car and jumped into the back.

Ian laughed. 'You've got them well trained.'

'I think they want to go home,' said Gerald. 'Thank you, Ian.'

'Yes, Ian, thanks a lot. I'm glad that's over for another year.'

When we got home I took them into the barn and gave them a bowl of nuts. But Pandora looked at me reproachfully. She had not enjoyed the dipping and I wondered when she would forgive me for refusing to help her when Ian's boot had been pushing her under the water.

The following afternoon I saw the school bus stop at the gate and Katy and Alex climbed down, carrying several bags of books between them. I thought at first that Tom had been left behind, and then I saw him scrambling down the steps holding what looked like an enormous, strange-shaped parcel. As they reached the gate I realised he was carrying a very large fawn-coloured goose. I ran out to meet them as Katy was opening the gate. The goose had a pointed orange beak and bright, inquisitive eyes. Tom had his left arm across its back and underneath it, and his right arm was holding the long neck to keep the beak away from his own face.

'Where did you find that?' I asked in amazement. 'It looks very heavy. Put it down or you'll hurt yourself.'

Tom deposited the goose on the ground and it flapped its wings and stretched out its neck and made some loud scolding noises.

'He came from the school,' said Tom. 'His mate got eaten by a fox and then all the chinese geese started chasing him. One of the masters was going to eat him for Michaelmas, so I asked if I could have him. I thought you wouldn't mind,' he added hopefully. 'He's quite a friendly goose, really.'

Katy was not so sure. 'He looks vicious to me,' she said. 'Look at that beak.'

'Oh, I think he's lovely,' I said, 'I've always liked geese. Poor old thing. I expect he was frightened of the bus. What did the driver say?'

Alex grinned. 'Well, he complained a bit and we thought he wouldn't let us on at first. But we said we had special permission from the headmaster.'

'Did you?'

'No. Luckily he didn't see us. He was busy in his study.'

The boys laughed, relieved to have rescued their goose and that I was so delighted to see it.

'Let's get him some food. Has he got a name? What are we going to call him?'

The goose stood in the midst of us, looking at each of us in turn, then scolded again. I went back towards the house with the children and the goose followed us, picking his way across the gravel on flat, rubbery feet. The dogs had heard the strange commotion going on outside and started barking. Henry was standing at the kitchen window with his front paws on the sill and his big black face staring out in surprise.

I pushed past the dogs, making sure that they did not get into the garden, and found a jar of corn from the pantry which I took back for our new arrival. He was standing at

the bottom of the steps with the children, as if he knew what I had gone to fetch. I tipped the corn out and he put his big orange beak down on the bricks and sucked it up like a vacuum cleaner. When he had finished he stretched his neck out again, flapped his wings and gave some more of his loud, raucous shouts.

There was an old tin bath behind the barn which Tom and Alex went to look for while I fixed the hose onto the outside tap. They dragged the bath to the back lawn and we filled it up with water. The goose kept near us, tipping his head on one side to look at us better with his bright, sharp eyes. He was very interested in the bath and kept craning his neck forward and peering in and making strange guttural sounds quietly in his throat.

When the bath was full we took the hose away and stepped back a little, and waited to see what he would do. He immediately put his beak into the water and sucked the water in and out through the serrated orange edges. Then he dipped his head and neck in and out repeatedly, making gurgling noises of delight. He then twisted his head round onto his back and pushed his beak through the ruffled feathers, into his wings, bobbing up and down as he did so. He was so happy with the bath. He stopped every so often and turned to look at us all, then went back to the important business of cleaning himself.

We left him to his bath and went into the house. The dogs had their noses glued to the edge of the door, sniffing noisily to try and catch the scent of whatever was now outside in their garden. I made some tea and toast and honey and we sat at the kitchen table with it. Suddenly there was a loud splash from outside. We all rushed to the window. The goose was bobbing about in the middle of the bath—his head proudly up, slightly on one side, so that the bright, shiny eyes could look at us all. He seemed delighted with his new home.

We decided to call the goose Gilbert. He was put into the barn for the night, with the doors shut to keep him safe from foxes. The swallows had long since flown their nest and I had not seen any at all flying around for the last two days, so perhaps they had left altogether until next spring.

In the morning I let him out and called him across to the steps where I had left him a pile of corn. It was soon gone, sucked up by the orange vacuum-cleaner beak, and then without any prompting he walked round the side of the cottage to the back lawn to find his bath. It had not taken him long to remember his way around.

Saturday morning saw the boys busy in the barn, constructing yet another animal house, this time for Gilbert. It was much simpler than the hen house—just a large wooden box which they set on bricks inside the barn, and a wire netting door. But with straw spread on its floor it made him a safe, dry shelter for the night and he soon learned to settle himself in there when it was getting dark. He would sit and mutter to himself and make quiet calls to us so that we should not forget to shut his door. But once shut in, he did not make another sound until morning.

And then it was time for Rodney and Melissa to go to America. The summer was over. The swallows had gone. We drove them to the airport, from the little cottage in Ickling Green with the honeysuckle round its door, through the neatly-hedged fields of Suffolk and Essex and, once through the tunnel, across the pale, rolling hills of Kent with its terraced hop fields and red-brick oast houses.

Rodney hugged me. 'Take care of yourself, old girl,' and then he and Melissa had gone, out of sight down the covered walkway to the departure lounge.

We went to the rooftop restaurant and Gerald fetched some coffee, but I could not drink mine. I sat with my eyes on the huge red and white plane marked 'American Airlines'. We saw the luggage loaded in, but the passengers boarded under cover. From our distance the portholes were tiny circles of glass, but I stood by the rail at the edge of the rooftop, waving and hoping that maybe Rodney would see me.

After what seemed hours but was probably about fifteen minutes, the engines were started and then slowly the plane began to move—to edge forward and turn towards

113

the runway. It nosed slowly along the tarmac like a huge, ponderous beast and I could not believe that Rodney and Melissa were somewhere hidden in its bowels. At last it reached the main runway and stood, engines roaring, waiting for a signal like greyhounds in the starting traps waiting to burst forward in a surge of energy.

I turned away, gripped by fear. I could not watch that rush forwards and the sudden lifting into the sky that always seemed so unbelievable.

'There they go,' shouted Tom excitedly. 'Goodbye, Uncle Rodney, goodbye, Auntie Melissa.'

'It's all right, Mother,' said Katy, her arm round me as I stood and sobbed.

'They've gone,' said Gerald. He glanced at me. 'They're safely up—you can look now. Good luck, Rodney and Melissa.'

I turned back to the runway. Already, in a few seconds, the plane was high and banking. It turned to the right of us and round in a half-circle, then headed away in a straight line to the west. I watched the speck grow smaller and smaller, straining my eyes at the spot where it had disappeared.

'I'll be back,' Rodney had said, 'I promise. I'll come back and buy a Norfolk farmhouse.' But at that moment I wondered if I should ever see him again. It seemed that I was losing my only real friend.

Gerald, in true English fashion, was somewhat embarrassed that I was still crying and was doubtless conscious of the curious glances from people sitting idly round the little tables with their coffee cups. Many of them were no doubt simply spending a pleasant morning watching the comings and goings of Gatwick Airport in general, rather than any departure in particular.

'Come and sit down over here,' he said gently, walking to a table at one side. 'I'll get some more coffee. Do you want anything to eat?'

Tom and Katy voted for some cakes but I shook my head. Tom went with Gerald to choose some and Katy and I sat at the table.

114

'Uncle Rodney said he's coming for a holiday next summer,' said Katy. 'That's not long. And you've got me and Tom. We'll look after you.'

I smiled at her then. 'I know. I'm sorry. I'm very lucky to have you two. I just wish Rodney wasn't going so far. I wanted him to go to Scotland.'

'I know,' she said.

Gerald and Tom returned with a tray of cups of coffee and cakes, and a large gin and tonic which Gerald put on the table in front of me.

'There you are,' he said, 'that should cheer you up.'

'Thanks, Gerald, you are a dear. It's just that America seems so far away.'

'Well, it's not really.' He was ever practical. 'It's only a ten-hour flight. It would take nearly that long to drive to Scotland. I think he's right to go. He has so much more opportunity out there. America has a lot more to offer him.'

Except itself, I thought.

That afternoon, back in the field with my beloved sheep, the morning seemed far away, unreal, like a dream. Berkeley sat chewing her cud and I sat with her, leaning against her back and threading daisies together. She watched through drowsy eyes as the plait grew longer. I put it over her head and round her neck, twisting the ends together, and she munched on. She looked so angelic sitting there, the daisies round her neck. Pandora was at a little distance, still grazing. Rodney and Melissa would be

115

half-way to Greenland and I was still sitting in my field with my sheep, as I had most of that summer. The little Tudor house and its meadow seemed to be more and more like a time warp. The world went on outside, but always there was the field and the sheep. I could go and sit there with them, and all the other things that had happened only seemed half-real. Like the games we had played as children, running round the playground chased by witches, wolves and bears, trying to reach the safe place first where they could not catch us.

I was beginning to feel that the field with the sheep was my safe place and that if I was there nothing could touch me or hurt me. Berkeley chewed on, the daisy chain round her neck.

Chapter Eight

Gilbert soon found his way round the garden, into all its corners, poking his orange beak under the hedge and into any old buckets or flower pots he found lying about. He answered to his name and as soon as he was called would come flapping across the garden, half-running, half-flying. He padded about the garden on his rubbery feet, eating the grass and Michaelmas daisies. Sometimes I would glance out of the window and see him standing looking at me, his head on one side and the bright, quizzical eyes peering in.

Sometimes he went up into the field, through a small hole he had found in a corner of the hedge. He could wriggle himself through and into the ditch the other side. If there was some water in the ditch he would stay there for hours, splashing and bobbing about in it. If the ditch was dry he scrambled up the bank and went running up to the chickens, calling and talking to them. But they seemed alarmed by his size and his loud voice and would run away, clucking and squawking. Poor Gilbert would then stand rather forlornly on his own, looking round for some other company. I was sure he was lonely.

I remembered a farm a few miles away that always seemed to have a field of geese, and sold geese ready dressed for the table. I decided I would go and find Gilbert a mate. The farmer was a charming old man, who had about fifty pure white geese in a field at the side of the farmhouse. He bought them as goslings from Norfolk every spring, he said, and fattened them up for Christmas. I explained that I wanted to buy a goose but not to eat for Christmas, simply as a mate for a gander that I had. I told him about Gilbert

117

and how friendly he was, but that I thought he was lonely.

'He keeps trying to make friends with the hens,' I said, 'but they think he's big and ugly and run away from him. I want to find a nice goose to keep him company.'

The old man scratched his head.

'Well,' he said, 'it seems to me you don't need anything fancy. One of these geese—well—I sell them by weight and they're big now—they'd cost you about £15; but I'm going to Chelmsford market tomorrow. I could get you an old goose there if you like.'

'Would you really? That would be wonderful.' I liked the idea of rescuing some poor, decrepit goose from the market. 'Are you sure it's no bother? It's very kind of you.'

'No trouble, my dear, since I'm going anyway. But you're sure you want one?'

'Oh, yes, definitely. A female goose, please.'

'Well, just give me your phone number, then, and when I get back from the market I'll give you a ring and you can come and fetch her.'

I was overjoyed. Tomorrow Gilbert would have a mate.

I waited all afternoon for the telephone to ring and began to think that maybe the old man had forgotten or not gone to the market after all. I had hoped to bring the new goose home and have her safely installed in the barn before Gerald came home. If I was just going out as he was coming in I should have some awkward explaining to do.

The old man phoned up as Gerald pulled into the gateway. I made him a cup of tea. 'Supper's almost ready. I'm just going out, but I won't be long. We can have it when I come back.'

'Where are you going?'

'Just somewhere. I won't be long.'

Gerald groaned. 'Not to fetch yet another beast, I hope. I feel like a game warden already. Simba have got in with the goats, bwana, God not again.' He said it in such a silly voice that we all started laughing.

I got out of the door as quickly as I could, before he asked any more questions. When I got to the farm it was dark. The farmer took me to one of the sheds near the house and picked up a large sack, out of which was poking a goose's head. She had a grey face and pale blue eyes, like kittens' eyes.

'There you are, my dear. She's just an ordinary old goose, but she'll be good company for your gander.'

'Oh, you are kind. She's lovely, thank you. How much do I owe you?'

'Well, it's five pounds, if that's all right. Perhaps you could drop the sack back some time when you're passing. Just put it over the wall. But they travel better like that —can't struggle and hurt themselves.'

I thought of Gilbert sitting up on the school bus, and wondered what he would say to that. The farmer carried the goose to the car for me and put her on the floor on the front passenger side. I drove home through the dark, wet lanes.

As I turned into the drive the front door opened and Gerald and the children came out, all curious to see what I had brought home. Gilbert was already in his house in the barn and the sheep were in their pen, their light still on, munching at their hay.

'I've got Gilbert a mate,' I said, opening the car door and lifting out the heavy sack. 'He's lonely.' Gerald took the sack and we went across to the barn, closing the heavy doors behind us. He put the sack down on the barn floor and untied the string around the top of it. The goose hardly moved. She just lay in the loose sack with her head on the floor.

'She's come from Chelmsford market,' I said. 'She looks quite exhausted, poor old thing. She's probably been tied up in that sack all afternoon and wondering what was going to happen to her.'

Gerald lifted her out of the sack and she sat in the straw and looked at us. Gilbert was peering out through his wire door, looking very excited. I took the water bucket out of the sheep's pen and put it beside her. She put her beak straight into it and took several long drinks, and then let the water dribble through the edges of her beak while she

119

dabbled it in the water. We opened the door of Gilbert's house and he flopped out and went up to the new goose almost shyly, making some soft, low noises to her and putting his beak down into the straw by her feet.

'She's pretty,' said Katy. 'Look at her lovely blue eyes. Let's call her Polly.'

'All right, Gilbert and Polly.'

I went back to the house and fetched a jar of corn. I put it into the straw by the geese's feet. Gilbert put his beak into it at once, and then stopped and waited for the new goose to have some corn. She looked at it for a few minutes and at us, then put her beak down and started eating. Gilbert joined in then, gobbling it up noisily.

We switched the light off and left them in the warm darkness of the barn, closing the heavy doors again as we went out. The new goose looked so tired I was sure she would put her head under her wing and go to sleep as soon as the light was out.

Next morning Gilbert and Polly were standing side by side as I opened the barn door, and Gilbert led her across to the doorstep for breakfast. He seemed so proud of her, and she followed him around all day. In the afternoon they sat together under the lilac bush, with their heads tucked into their wings. Polly appeared to be asleep, but Gilbert's head was only half under his wing, and a bright, beady eye was wide open and watching everything that went on.

I thought of asking Laura and Primrose, Ian's wife, to come and have coffee, so I dialled Ian's number. He answered. He had a very seductive telephone voice, which I had remarked on to Laura. She had only laughed and said she had never noticed. I listened now to the alluring, well-spoken tones as he talked about sheep and asked how my two were behaving themselves.

'I'm sending the sheep to the Bury Sheep Sales on Wednesday,' he continued.

'What, all of them?' I asked, surprised. 'Aren't you going to keep sheep any more?'

I felt dismayed. I could not imagine Ian without his sheep, and I had hoped to have another bottle lamb from

120

him next spring, though naturally I had not mentioned it to Gerald. Time enough for that, I had thought, when he came home and found another lamb in the kitchen. But where was I to get one if Ian no longer had any sheep?

'I'll still have sheep, but not here,' he went on. 'I'm going to the farm in Scotland.'

'Oh, Ian, when are you going? Are you going for good?'

'Lizzy, Lizzy, all these questions.' He paused. 'I'm probably going in a couple of weeks. At the moment I don't know how long for.'

He sounded strange, different from usual, quieter but with a suppressed sense of excitement. He did not mention Primrose and I had a feeling he was going without her. I could not imagine her burying herself away from civilisation and did not ask to speak to her. My desire to invite her for coffee had gone. Instead I went to see Laura. She knew all the village comings and goings far better than I did. Most of them were of no interest to me.

'Ian told me he's going to Scotland in a couple of weeks.'

'Yes,' she said, making two mugs of coffee. 'You know they've got another farm up there, with three thousand sheep? Well he's leaving Primrose and going with some woman from the village. Apparently they've been seeing each other all summer.'

I was stunned. 'I don't believe it. Who is she?'

'She's been renting a house near the green since Easter. She came from Wiltshire.'

'What about Primrose? What is she going to do?' Primrose, always smart and elegant, the girl from the town, whom I had never really liked. I found her reserved and awkward to talk to. I remembered then how I had never seen Primrose near the sheep. The day I had gone to fetch Pandora she had been in the garden pruning the roses and wearing rubber gloves. I despised people who wore rubber gloves for gardening—it was bad enough to wear them for washing-up. How ill-suited she and Ian must have been, and I wondered why they had ever married.

'She will stay where she is for now, with the children, but I think it's going to be difficult for her. She won't go to the

121

village at all at the moment as she feels everyone is talking about her.'

'I'm sure they are,' I said heartily, hating Primrose at that moment and wishing that Ian had married me instead of her. Laura was far more charitable than I and felt genuinely sorry for her.

'Oh, Laura, I wish I'd known Ian wanted someone to run away with. I'd have gone with him.'

Laura looked surprised. 'Are you serious?'

'I wish I was going to Scotland with Ian. Oh, it's not fair. I wish I'd known sooner. I'd have gone to see him and his sheep more often. I never imagined Ian would leave the farm. He seemed so respectable, so settled.'

'What about Gerald?' asked Laura.

'Gerald will never go to Scotland. I've tried to persuade him before. I've always wanted to go.'

For the rest of the day I could think of nothing but the fact that Ian was going to Scotland—to the wild empty places, to the purple hills where I longed to go. Ian was going and I would be left behind in the cosy commuter country of North Essex, with its thatched cottages and neatly hedged fields, and I would probably never see him again.

I was not in love with Ian, but I was in love with his way of life—with the thought of life on the heather hills surrounded by sheep. The very word 'Scotland' held a special magic for me—the mist-covered hills and empty spaces. I loved the sound of Scottish voices and the music of bagpipes. My grandmother had been Scottish and I had often longed to go and live there myself.

I had tried years before to persuade Gerald to take a job in Edinburgh, but it had been useless. Gerald had been born in Essex and lived there all his life. He was tied to the salt marshes and the strawberry fields as I was drawn to the hills and moors.

I went out to the field and took some biscuits in my pocket, and Pandora and Berkeley followed me to the top of the meadow. I sat under the oak tree and watched them grazing near me. We had sat there in the summer among the clover blossoms and moon daisies, and I had thought then that this place had seemed perfect. But now the air was chill. The gold and brown leaves were blowing along the wind, and far away at the back of my mind was a new restlessness.

A few mornings later, Tom and Katy were rushing about finding their books for school and I was feeding Gilbert and Polly on the doorstep, when I saw the school bus trundle past the gate and on down the lane. Tom and Katy rushed out of the front door in time to see its disappearing red-and-cream back-view as it turned a corner and vanished.

'Oh, no,' said Katy, 'it must have been early today.'

'Never mind, I'll run you into school. We'll be there before the bus, anway. Let's have a cup of coffee first.' The bus took half an hour to reach the school which was five miles away. It wound backwards and forwards through the lanes, past lonely farm tracks and through several villages, collecting the children as it went.

We arrived at the school in plenty of time. I left them at the gate and set off home again, through the lanes, full of wet, brown leaves. The hedges were gold and brown, dotted with red hips and strewn with strings of scarlet briony berries and fluffy grey tufts of old man's beard. A cloud of fieldfares flew up from the berries and clattered away in alarm.

Then I saw ahead of me a large, dark red cattle float. I slowed down, as I did not want to catch up with it. I had a horror of those hideous wagons taking some poor, gentle, unsuspecting creatures to their deaths—taking them to the awful nightmare of noise and blood and knives. Then I saw that it was in fact a sheep transporter with an open top—to stack the sheep in three rows, with those on top open to the wind and rain and air. I always wondered why they did not leap off in panic to their deaths on the road below.

Ahead of it was a second transporter, and they both appeared to be empty. I followed them to within half a mile of Monk's Green and then turned down our lane, leaving them to wind their way onwards, and wondered where they could be going. Then I remembered Ian and the fact that it was Wednesday, market day in Bury St Edmunds.

The lorries must be going to fetch all his sheep and take them to the big autumn sheep sales there. I did not know why I had not realised it sooner and I had a terrible feeling of panic. They seemed like horrible great dragons scouring the countryside for any sheep they could find, and I wanted to rush home quickly and hide Pandora and Berkeley until the danger had passed. I wished I could have saved Ian's sheep from going to market, too, but there was nothing I could do.

When I got home I went to the meadow to sit with Pandora and Berkeley. They came up to me and Berkeley sat down beside me and started chewing her cud. I stroked her smooth, black face. 'Poor sheep,' I whispered sadly, 'all those poor sheep being sent away.' Their mothers and their sisters were going. I remembered Pandora's mother with her pale eyes, and wished that I could have saved her. Only Pandora and Berkeley would be left. The Jacob ewes might be sold to other breeders, but certainly all the cross-bred lambs like Berkeley would be sold for meat, and all the little wethers.

There had been so many lambs running round the yard that day when I had chosen her. She munched on, unaware of the unhappy fate of her erstwhile companions, a contented look in her golden-brown eyes. Perhaps she did not even remember them now. She and Pandora were always together. The only flock she had now was one other lamb and a rather eccentric human being.

There was a letter from Rodney that morning. He and Melissa were in Dallas and had been looking at some plots of land out of town on which to build their house. They had found one they liked thirty-four miles from Dallas in a place called Poetry. It was east of Dallas on the least-travelled roads, and it would take about forty minutes to drive in to work in the mornings, but he felt it would be worth it. The place was very pretty and secluded.

They would have to clear a space to build the house. East of Dallas was the flat, treeless land where cotton was grown, and they had gone as far as a change of soil and the treeline. There were deer there and wild turkeys and lots of lizards, and he had also seen armadilloes. Rodney sounded really excited about it and I hoped that they would be happy there.

Texas was six thousand miles away and I wished they had gone to Scotland: Aberdeen was only half a day away. But, unlike me, Rodney had no longings to live in Scotland. He hated the cold, damp mist and longed for the sun.

He wrote about the birds he had seen—something bright and exotic-looking like a zoo escapee, he said, with red belly, green wings and blue cap. There were beautiful birds called scarlet tamarinds and red-winged blackbirds. He said there were butterflies everywhere. The one we call the Camberwell Beauty, which is uncommon here, was in abundance there, although he had not yet discovered its Texas name. The Monarch butterfly migration had started, and the large, beautiful orange butterflies were everywhere. They flew south thousands of miles each year to Mexico for the winter. Rodney told me to look in my butterfly book for them, under milkweed as that was their food plant. They were a rare migrant to Britain.

Our days were short and getting colder. Some nights there was frost, but he said the temperature there was about 85°F and had been 100°F when they landed three weeks ago. He had enclosed a leaflet on the agricultural ratings of Texas in the USA, as he thought I would be interested to learn that it was first in sheep and wool production. It was also first in mohair production, with Dallas being the mohair capital of the world. There were about one and a half million mohair goats in Texas and he said that when they had their house and land they might get a couple of mohair goats themselves, and would send me some fleece to spin.

It was strange to think of him so far away, in such a different environment. My mind drifted back to the hot, sandy scrub of West Africa, the scarlet flame of the forest flowers, the iridescent humming birds and pink and green chameleons.

I looked up the butterflies in my books, one of which had been given to me by Rodney. They were both there—

Camberwell Beauty described as a rare visitor from Scandinavia and known there and in America as the Mourning Cloak butterfly. There was a whole page devoted to the Monarch and its sex life and powers of flight. At one time it was thought that the Monarch came to England from its breeding grounds in the Canary Islands, but apparently it had now been proved that the Monarch butterflies actually flew across the Atlantic from America, an amazing feat for something seemingly so fragile. It was said to be the only representative in England of the danaids, the name coming from the habit of the males when making love to hover over their intended mate, scattering her with scented dust, alluding to the Greek myth of the imprisoned maiden Danae being visited by Zeus, king of the gods, in a shower of gold.

I had always marvelled at the ability of butterflies to fly across the Channel from the continent. There were a great many small tortoiseshells spreading their wings now in the sun on the Michaelmas daisies under the kitchen window, and with them were several Red Admiral butterflies that must have found their way here from France, but to fly several thousand miles across the Atlantic seemed unbelievable.

I sat with the books in the autumn sun on the bench

under the window and read on, watching the butterflies and forgetting all about Ian and his sheep.

I did not see Ian again, but next time I saw Laura she told me he had left. Rodney and Melissa had gone, Ian had gone. Life kept changing all the time, like cloud patterns in the sky, like the patterns on the sand left by the waves washing in and out. Always the same, yet always changing.

The fields around us had all been ploughed now, and were brown instead of yellow. There were dark, wet leaves along the hedges. There were still some blackberries about, but they were shrivelled and woody. The devil was supposed to spit on them at Michaelmas and make them unfit to eat. Something had certainly spoiled them, so we had no more blackberry pies.

October began with clear, bright days, still quite warm at noon, but the morning air smelled of frost and the evenings were damp and misty. Pandora and Berkeley went into the barn now at tea-time and settled in the straw with a pile of hay. When they were let into the field in the morning, after eating the nuts out of their bowls, they walked along beside the hedge, nibbling up all the yellow and gold leaves that had fallen in the night.

The second weekend in October there was an autumn show at Peterborough, at the East of England Showground, exhibiting poultry, rabbits, goats and rare breeds of sheep, as well as various craft stalls. I thought it might be fun to go, but Gerald was not very interested and Tom wanted to spend his Saturday playing football with Alex in Castle Monkton. So Katy and I set off together after breakfast and, reaching the M11 at Wetherbury, soon afterwards joined the A1 and arrived at the showground.

We came to the goat tent first, but they never seem to have quite the same appeal to me as sheep. I know that goats are intelligent and affectionate, but they often have weird owners—young men with rope sandals and beards who smell like their goats, or earnest middle-aged spinster ladies who wear sensible shoes and no make-up. And goat owners always seem unfriendly, reluctant to admit would-be novice goat owners into their select circle.

Sheep owners, on the other hand, seemed to be gregarious and extrovert, sitting around in groups at agricultural shows amidst bottles of whisky and much laughter. We soon left the goat lines in search of sheep.

There were plenty of different breeds; primitive Soays, spaniel-sized and looking like little antelopes; black and white Jacobs; soft-woolled gentle-faced Shetlands; black Hebrideans, the rams with four large horns looking as forbidding as Gerda's 'Little Yeacoub'. Then we came to a pen of three small, white hornless sheep with wool on their faces and legs, giving them the appearance of teddy bears. They were enchanting. As I leaned over the hurdles I was aware of Katy nudging me and, turning round, I looked up into the smiling face of David Roberts, the blue-eyed farmer I had met at the school fête.

'Hello,' he said easily, 'it's the lady with the alcoholic sheep, isn't it? Where is your wayward beast today?'

I smiled. 'I've left her at home.'

'Very prudent. Are you spinning here?'

'No, I've just come to look at the sheep. Are these Southdowns?'

'No, they're Ryelands. Southdowns are similar but smaller, and of course they do not have such good wool.'

I had heard of Ryelands, of course, famed in the Middle Ages for the fineness of their wool, but had not seen any in real life before. They originated in the rye-growing areas of Herefordshire—hence their name—bred by monks in the land around Leominster. In the Middle Ages, when the wealth of England was built on wool, still symbolised by the Woolsack, seat of England's Chancellor, barons, bishops and abbots had flocks counted in thousands and tens of thousands, producing the finest wool in Europe to supply the woollen industries of Italy and Holland. And the most prized wool came from the Ryeland, known as 'Lemster Or'. With the decline of the woollen industry and the production of sheep mainly for meat instead of wool, as in medieval England, the Ryeland had lost popularity, being

128

replaced by quick-maturing breeds of sheep. Their numbers had fallen so drastically that they were now on the rare breed list, although David told me that they were now increasing again and would be off the list next year. He said they were docile, easily handled and did not have the foot and lambing problems of some of the other breeds. I would have loved to bundle one into the car and take it home, but I thought of Gerald and decided against the idea.

'A Ryeland ram would be ideal for your two ewes. Why don't you want to breed from them? Sheep enjoy lambing, they have strong mothering instincts. And think of all the lambs you could have.'

'If they kept having lambs I'd run out of room to keep them all.'

'You don't keep the lambs, you sell them.' He looked at me in some surprise. Surely I realised that?

'Well,' I said, 'I wouldn't like to sell them. I don't eat meat. I wouldn't eat them myself, and I wouldn't like someone else eating them.'

He looked amused. 'Oh you're a vegetarian, then?' He looked me up and down and then just stood smiling, his eyes on my face.

'There wouldn't be any sheep if people didn't eat them. You wouldn't have your two lambs. A sheep's one ambition is to die before its time, we're only helping them along.'

'What do you mean?' I saw the laughter in his blue eyes. He's teasing me, I thought, he must think I'm stupidly sentimental.

'If I didn't keep watching them, just think of all the things that would happen to them. They'd get foot-rot and blowfly. They'd tangle themselves up in the brambles. They'd soon die if they were just left to themselves. All sheep have a death wish—ask any shepherd.'

'Oh, don't say that.' Perhaps he was right. Sometimes they did seem to give up so hopelessly, and just die.

'So you don't want one of my rams?'

'Do you have any bottle lambs in the spring? I'd love a Ryeland lamb. They are beautiful little sheep.'

'We usually have a few Ryeland lambs. You can certainly have one if you like. It will be about March. I've got your number somewhere but you'd better give it to me again. If you haven't heard from me by the middle of March, ring me. I'm very forgetful.'

'All right,' I said, but I did not think he would forget, any more than I would.

Chapter Nine

Winter had really come now. The wind was howling round the little house and whistling through the keyhole and some cracks round the old door. It sounded like the setting for some ghostly story. In the Middle Ages they had blocked the keyholes with fennel to keep out the ghosts, but Berkeley had eaten all the fennel.

The leaves had gone, whipped away by the wind's fury, but some spindle berries still clung to the bare branches. They stood out, starkly pink against the dark hedge. I watched some seagulls flying backwards, being tossed over the ploughed fields. The wind shook the willows and the poplars to their very roots, and I wondered if the poplars would come down. I hoped that they would be blown towards the field and not the house.

There were still plenty of large orange rose hips in the hedge, as well as the spindle berries, and I thought idly that I should make them into jelly. But the thought of having to go out in the cold to gather them sapped my enthusiasm. Later . . . tomorrow, perhaps . . . or the next day. The little house was warm and cosy despite the wind, and the dogs and cats were all asleep on the rug near the Aga.

Pandora and Berkeley were standing sadly beside their gate, wondering where their summer had gone. Unless it was raining heavily I put them into the meadow every day. I had read that sheep needed to walk at least a quarter of a mile every day to aid their digestion, to make sure that the curious process of chewing their cud functioned properly. But they did not like the wind: it seemed to make them uneasy. They wandered about a little and nibbled at the remains of the grass, and then returned to stand by their gate and munch at the pile of hay I had put for them.

I decided to put them into the barn earlier than usual and went out with their bowls of nuts, and some corn for Gilbert and Polly. The geese were sitting, heads under wings, under the lilac bush, and came flapping and shouting now to the doorstep for their tea. I put the bowls of sheep nuts into the barn and put fresh hay into their hay rack, then ran round the corner of the house to their gate. Pandora was looking over it hopefully, with ears forward; no doubt she had heard me in the barn and realised it was nearly supper time. She called out eagerly as soon as she saw me, relief and desperation in her voice, as well as the customary greeting.

'Come on, my poor darlings, you can go in early tonight.' I opened the gate and they pushed forward, trotted round the corner of the house and disappeared.

I went into the field to the hens. After their breakfast they had retreated back inside their house for the day. They appeared in the doorway and hopped down as I threw some corn on the ground for them, their feathers blown, their tails nearly inside out.

I went back to the barn. Pandora and Berkeley had emptied their bowls of nuts and stood in the corner, pulling at the hay and looking pleased to be out of the wind. I stood and watched them eating, enormous now in their winter fleeces, and found it difficult to believe that the huge, shaggy brown and white beast I was watching had been a tiny black and white lamb less than nine months ago. Something so small and fragile that I had been entrusted to care for, so afraid that I should fail. Now she was a long-woolled sheep, nearly as large as her mother had been. Although she and Berkeley would not be classed as sheep until they had been sheared in another five or six months' time, looking at them now as they munched their hay they seemed at last two big, healthy sheep, and I hoped I should have them for many years to come. They had given me so much pleasure over that summer, sitting in the meadow with them, walking along the lane, watching them eating flowers. There was something infinitely pleasing to me about keeping an animal that lived off flowers and not the dead bodies of other animals. I had always liked sheep, but until I had actually owned these two had never imagined just how delightful they were. They were warm and gentle and loving, and there was nothing about them that one could possibly dislike. Most things seem to have disadvantages, but sheep to me were perfect.

My thoughts were interrupted by honking in the barn doorway, and Gilbert appeared, followed by Polly. They had finished their tea on the doorstep and now found their way to the barn for the night.

'Hello, Gilbert,' I said. He put his head a little on one side and stared at me with his bright eyes. He then walked over to their little house and, after stretching his neck and making a great deal of noise, poking his beak first into the house and then towards Polly, he finally jumped clumsily in, followed with much flapping and squawking by his mate. I shut their door.

'Goodnight, Gilbert, goodnight, Polly.'

He gave a series of loud replies, scolding, it seemed, everyone. Polly answered once.

I turned back to the sheep. They were quiet and happy. I left them to their hay and ran back across the garden to the field and the poor, ruffled hens. They were now back in their house and I shut their door until morning.

I went back into the cottage and put the kettle on, and by the time I had made some tea the school bus had trundled to a halt at the gate. Katy and Tom ran up the path. They burst in through the door into the warm house and went to the Aga to warm themselves.

'Hello, darlings, how was school? There's a cup of tea ready,' and I took it over to them.

'School was awful,' said Katy, 'we had geography.' She groaned. The geography teacher and Katy had a clash of personalities.

'I had a good day,' said Tom. 'We had a debate about animals in class, and I stood up and said I thought keeping battery hens was disgusting.'

134

'Oh, did you? Well done!' I felt very proud that he not only thought that but had the courage to stand up and say so in front of thirty other people.

Katy spread her homework books out on the table and Tom went into the sitting-room to switch on the television and watch his favourite cartoons.

I went out to the barn again. Pandora and Berkeley were sitting together in the straw, watching the doorway, having heard my steps on the gravel. Their ears were forward, their faces inquisitive, but the busy jaws were moving rhythmically. They had started on the serious business of cud chewing.

'Good night, Pandora, good night, Berkeley,' I said to them as always, switching off their light and then running back to the cottage.

I fed the cats and dogs and then began preparing our supper. I washed some vegetables and put them ready to cook, scrubbed some potatoes and put them to bake in the Aga. Then I joined Tom in the sitting-room in time to watch the news and weather. The news showed motorists stranded in snow drifts whipped up by strong winds. The weather map looked forbidding, all depressions, criss-crossed by isobars. I offered a silent, useless prayer for Monk's Green to be spared from snow. Scotland, it seemed, was very badly affected. All but the main roads were blocked by snow and farmers were shown digging ewes out of drifts. I thought again of Ian and wondered where he was and what he was doing.

Gerald was usually in soon after the weather forecast had finished, but three quarters of an hour later he was still not home. If he had late meetings he always phoned to let me know and, as the minutes ticked noisily away on the grandfather clock, I began to wonder if he had had an accident.

'Father's late,' said Katy, struggling with her physics homework.

'I expect he'll be here soon. He must have been held up by something,' I said, not wanting to worry her.

Just then I saw the car headlights at the gate and Gerald

135

turned into the drive. He came in looking cold and tired and went across to the Aga to warm himself.

'Are you all right?' I asked, handing him a cup of coffee. 'We were getting worried about you.'

'I thought you'd had an accident,' said Katy.

'It's a terrible night out there,' he said. 'There was a tree down across the road on that sharp corner by the mill. I was so nearly home, and then I had to turn back and go round through the village, which must have taken me another five or six miles. I was just thinking I'd soon be home by the Aga in a nice warm house.' He drank the coffee, still standing in his thick grey overcoat. 'There's a forecast of snow on the way, too. I wouldn't be surprised if we're snowed in by the morning. How have you all been today? I was worried about the poplars. I hope they won't blow down on the house.'

'So do I,' said Katy, 'since they're next to my bedroom.'

Gerald smiled at her. 'Don't worry, Katy. They'd go the other way towards the field if they did blow down; that's the way the wind is blowing. I was just thinking about them today, that's all. I think there will be a lot of trees down tonight, though. But at least we're all safe and warm.'

He took off his coat then, and sat on the settle to finish his coffee. 'Poor old Katy, you're always doing homework. What have you got tonight?'

'Lots as usual,' said Katy, sighing. 'I'm doing physics at the moment, but I'm a bit stuck. Can you help me with it after supper?'

'Yes, of course,' he replied.

It began snowing soon after ten o'clock that evening. Great white flakes that quickly put a covering on everything. The dogs went out and looked at it in surprise, sniffing at the cat tracks running across the steps. They were not out long and came in with their backs white from the flakes. They had left big pad prints on the doorstep, but ten minutes later these had vanished under the still falling snow.

Next morning the wind had dropped, and there had not been as much snow in the night as we had anticipated.

136

Everywhere was white, but it had blown off the trees so that they stood out starkly, and cars kept passing along the lane. Gerald left for work as usual and the school bus collected Tom and Katy from the gate. But the sky was grey-white and looked full of snow, and I was sure we should have some more. It was there, just waiting to maroon us all.

I let the sheep out of their pen and they stood in the doorway looking out at the snow. It was something they had never seen before and they looked at it and then at me inquiringly, and then back at the snow. Then Berkeley remembered her breakfast and made her way to the field. I let Gilbert and Polly out, and Gilbert seemed quite excited by the snow. He rubbed his beak in it and bobbed up and down, rubbing his beak over his back and through his wings, the way that he did when he found a large puddle on the drive or water in the ditch.

But the poor hens did not like the snow at all. I cleared it away from around their house with a shovel and sprinkled their corn on the ground, but as soon as they had finished eating they scrambled back inside their house.

Pandora and Berkeley seemed to like the snow. They nibbled and licked at it for some time, and then started running about after each other and jumping in the air. Berkeley's jumps were not very high, but Pandora jumped and skipped about the way she had as a tiny lamb, jumping up facing one way and landing facing a different direction.

There were lots of little bird tracks criss-crossing in the snow, and rabbit tracks along the hedge near the oak tree. Pandora and Berkeley left heart-shaped hoof prints every-where they walked, and round near the house, over the dogs' pad marks, were big, flat triangles from the webbed feet of Gilbert and Polly.

It began snowing again in the middle of the morning. Not the large flakes of the night before, but small, hard, icy flakes, like tiny lumps of crystal. It snowed intermittently all day until the school bus came back to the gate. But the lane was still black tarmac where cars had passed along it, and it looked as if our fears of being snowed in had been groundless.

After dark, however, the snow flakes grew larger again and the wind strengthened. The snow piled up against the doorsteps and covered the bottom of the door and the window panes. When we woke up next morning the snow was three feet deep in the drive, and we had to dig a path across to the barn and dig the snow away from the doors before I could get in to Pandora and Berkeley. The trees were strange white shapes, glistening magically, piled up with snow so that the branches drooped with the weight and some of them touched the ground. The lane was blocked. The snow had blown off the field opposite in the night and piled up against the banks, so that it was six feet deep in places.

Tom and Katy were full of excitement. There was no way they could get to school today. I fed Pandora and Berkeley in the barn. They would have to stay in all day, perhaps for several days. They would disappear from view in the drifts along the hedge of their meadow. Gilbert and Polly were let out of their house, but they stayed in the barn all day, Gilbert going to the doorway often and stretching out his long neck and scolding.

As soon as we had finished breakfast, Tom and Katy were outside. At the corner of the lane, where we turned to Castle Monkton, there was a small hill, and they grabbed the largest tray we had and went running down the lane, slipping and falling in the deep snow with much laughing and shouting. They spent the morning taking it in turns to slide down the hill on the tray. Gerald and I shovelled and brushed the snow away from the doors and cleared a better path to the barn. I scraped away a space on the back lawn and put food out for the birds. I had seen only one solitary blackbird, but they appeared as if from nowhere—noisy starlings, little fluffed-up sparrows, shy robins and blackbirds. There were greenfinches, too, and blue tits, and they all scrambled and squabbled over the food. Some fieldfares came and sat on the hedge at the back of the lawn, but did not dare to venture so near the house. I took more bread and corn out and put some at the base of the hedge. The fieldfares retreated when I went out, but after I had gone back into the house I watched from the window and saw them return and start pecking at it, soon joined by some blackbirds.

The dogs loved the snow. The spaniel made great leaps up and down in it, disappearing from view each time and then reappearing, her golden ears flying as she jumped. The two big dogs put their noses into all the holes in the snow, sniffing and snorting noisily to get all the smells trapped there—the smells of cats and birds and mice. They ran about waving their tails and lifting their legs against snow-covered bushes and tree trunks, making yellow stains in the pure whiteness.

I telephoned the school, but they said that only the children who lived right near it in the village had been able to get there that morning, and they had been sent home again. All the school buses were snowed in, in their garage, and the school was closed.

The next day a snow plough came down the lane and cleared a single track, piling the snow at the sides of the lane into a great white wall. But no cars came down the lane. Tom and Katy had snowball fights and made a huge snow teddy bear near the front gate, and slid down the hill on their tea tray.

Pandora and Berkeley stayed in their warm barn, munching hay. I walked up the meadow, wading through the

snow, looking at all the little tracks dotting the smooth, white expanse. All that whiteness made my eyes hurt; the snow seemed stifling and suffocating. I wondered what it would be like to be lost in the snow, to walk on and on in this terrible white sea. I thought about Captain Oates, a story that had always somehow frightened me, and wondered how he had felt. The snow seemed to drain one's energy, numb one's mind. I hated the snow.

Three mornings later we woke to the sound of rain on the window and, looking out, there were vast expanses of green all over the meadow and on the lawn and the drive, like oases in a desert. The trees and hedges were black, dripping with rain drops. Life had returned to normal.

There were only a few weeks to Christmas now. We went to Cambridge one Saturday to do some Christmas shopping. The shops were bright and warm, the market full of stalls with blue and white striped awning.

Two students were busking in the shopping arcade. A young man with soft brown hair was playing the violin and a dark-eyed girl was playing the flute. The music echoed round the market square. They played a piece of Dvorak's 'New World'—my favourite part of it, a little sad, a little haunting. This was one of the things I loved about Cambridge. There were usually musicians in the arcade: I always looked for them and I had seen these two before. The music was very beautiful and I could have stood and listened to them all day. They gave a special magic to our shopping expedition.

I bought some books as presents: a book about cats for Melissa and one about Queen Victoria for my mother. Inspired by the lovely music, I bought a record of Vivaldi flute concertos for Meg. We wondered round the market and I bought lots of vegetables—our staple diet—peppers, celery, aubergines and tangerines, and chestnuts to roast on the open fire on Sunday afternoon.

They were selling fresh dates, so I bought a pound of those as well. The sticky, sweet, squashed concoctions sold in boxes as dates bear little resemblance to the fresh ones: they are a delight to eat. We used to have them in the

Middle East and I have always loved dates. They brought back to mind the empty expanses of sandy waste, the irrigation ditches swimming with turtles, the doves cooing in the olive groves and, of course, the tall date palms. By the time we had arrived home the bag of dates was empty.

We drove home leaving the grey spires of Cambridge behind in the gathering dusk, over the blue-grey, rolling hills, wreathed in bands of silver mist. The sky changed from grey to pink, and then blue-purple. The spire of Wetherbury church stood out ahead, golden lights from the little cottages round it, dotted in the mist like stars.

Pandora and Berkeley were standing anxiously by the gate when we got home, waiting to go into the warmth of the barn and their hay. They called out through the darkness as we got out of the car.

The following week I bought a Christmas tree in Castle Monkton, and Tom and Katy spent a happy afternoon decorating it. We put it in the sitting-room whence animals were officially banned, as I knew what would happen if it was in a corner of the kitchen. The cats would be scaling its branches, leaping among the tinsel and playing pawball with the glass baubles.

'There, how does it look?' They stood back and admired their handiwork.

'Lovely,' I said.

'Can we have one of the chocolates?' asked Tom. They had just finished tying them all on.

'And the dogs?' said Katy. 'Let's give them one, too?'

The dogs had been lying in wait outside the door, and they nearly fell into the room when the door was opened. Sophie ran to the Christmas tree immediately. She got most excited about Christmas and loved the rustling of paper and snuffling chew sticks and chocolate buttons out of the sock that was always hung on the fireplace for her on Christmas Eve. The big dogs sat with thick tails swishing across the carpet. Katy untied the gold threads. Sophie leaped up and down eagerly. The chocolates disappeared down their cavernous throats so quickly, I wondered if they had tasted them at all.

142

On Christmas Eve I went out to the barn to Pandora and Berkeley, last thing at night before I went to bed. They came up to me and I stroked their soft noses, felt their warm breath on my hand. Sheep had been in the stable on that first Christmas, and all down the centuries they had been the symbol of peace and love. 'Happy Christmas, sheep,' I whispered to them, into the darkness.

Christmas Day was warm and mild. We had nut roast for lunch, made with chestnuts, celery and mushrooms, and everyone agreed it was delicious. After lunch we went for a walk with the dogs and Pandora and Berkeley. The grass beside the road, that had been full of flowers in the summer, was now wet and lying in yellow clumps, strewn with brown leaves that had fallen from the hedge. Pandora and Berkeley sniffed at it and took a few nibbles, but mostly were just content to walk along the road with us, Pandora swishing her long tail as she walked and tossing her head a little.

At the corner we turned up the little hill that Tom and Katy had slid down on their tea tray a few weeks ago in all the snow. There were already a few purple violets in bloom, growing among the moss at the foot of an old ash tree. At the top we came to the treeless lane that led to Castle Monkton, and there was the castle standing out in grey splendour on the skyline.

The air was still and smelled of spring. The fields were already growing green again with winter wheat. Another year was nearly over.

Chapter Ten

We did not have any more snow that winter, but we had days of endless rain that kept Pandora and Berkeley in their pen in the barn, munching mounds of hay.

Gilbert and Polly were delighted. The ditch at the back of the garden, that ran along the hedge separating the lawn from the meadow, was now about three feet deep in water and filled Gilbert with joy. He wriggled through the hole in the corner of the hedge that he had found earlier, when he had gone to try and make friends with the hens, and he swam up and down calling loudly to Polly to join him. She waddled about on the back lawn making answering calls, but seemed reluctant to push through the hedge. Eventually she walked up past the apple tree and through the little gate into the meadow, which had been left open, and then half-ran, half-slithered down the bank to join Gilbert. They swam backwards and forwards along the ditch together, making happy little squawks to each other.

The hens stood in the doorway of their house, wet and bedraggled, looking out at the grey sky and watching the geese in silence. The dark hedge was grey-brown and lifeless, hanging with drops of moisture, like tears.

Rodney wrote about their rains, too. They had had eight inches in one day and some very bad flooding. He said that a lot of people had been drowned while driving. They had suddenly found their cars windshield-high in water and, on getting out, had been swept away by the current. There was a small zoo in a place called Graham, where he often went to inspect the oil rigs. When the floods came the zoo had released the animals and rounded them up again later after the water subsided. Luckily they did not have any lions or tigers. Most of the animals, he said, had survived, although a few deer and sheep had drowned. The llama was seen strutting down the highway, and monkeys and bears were in trees.

The only animal that they had been unable to find was Gerry, the elephant. They found him, on the second day, only his trunk visible, sticking out of the water. He was tangled up in a tree, in the branches and debris that had been washed along by the flood waters, but had survived. Rodney said the zoo had started selling T-shirts with Gerry's picture on, to raise money to rebuild the zoo.

Then the sun came out again. Tom busied himself on Saturday digging in a corner of the field to make his own vegetable patch. He was going to grow lettuces and radishes for me, he said, but mainly corn and potatoes for his hens. Pandora and Berkeley were now officially no longer lambs. They would be hoggets until they were shorn and were certainly as fat as the proverbial pig, although all the pigs I have seen tend to be on the lean side, and it is sheep who are fat.

They had lovely thick fleeces and I thought with pleasure of spinning them. Pandora's wool was a good six inches long, and a mixture now of black, white, grey and brown. It was very soft, and next to her pink skin was so white. Where she had black wool, her skin was dark, too, purple-grey.

I still had some of Ian's fleeces left, and I spun and knitted a jersey for Tom from some Jacob wool, twisting one thread of black and one thread of white together on the wheel to make a tweed mixture. It looked very attractive knitted up, and was very warm. I also made him a dark brown jerkin, and wearing them both to do his digging he had no need of a coat.

Pandora and Berkeley started having mock battles, prancing about in the field and then putting their heads down and running and butting each other as rams do. Pandora's horns were now about seven inches long and

145

146

looked very menacing, giving her an advantage, but Berkeley certainly had the weight.

The following weekend Tom and Alex disappeared up the meadow to the tree house, taking Henry and Wolf with them. I watched them going through the grass from an upstairs window, two boys and two big dogs all running happily, all keeping together, and, jumping and skipping about after them, were the two sheep. When they got to the oak tree at the top of the meadow I could just see the boys' silhouettes as they climbed the ladder. Pandora and Berkeley then turned and started running back towards the gate as fast as they could, Pandora in the lead. They stopped by the apple tree and Berkeley stood panting, quite out of breath from her exertion.

The dogs stayed up near the tree and sat down in the grass, watching Tom and Alex. The four of them stayed there all morning. Every time I went to look from the window I could see the dogs wandering about under the tree with their tails waving. The sheep had lost interest in them; they had wandered to the hedge at the side and were nibbling at fresh young shoots of cow parsley and new leaves on the blackberry stems.

The boys and the dogs reappeared at lunchtime, asking for a picnic to take back to the tree house. I gave them some coffee and baked potatoes and chocolate cake, and they collected a hammer and some nails from the barn.

'You can come up and see the house if you like,' Tom invited.

'All right, I'll be up later, when we've had lunch.'

I walked up through the damp grass after lunch. Tom and Alex waved from the oak tree and the dogs watched me from the bottom of the tree, waving their tails and showing their teeth.

I climbed up the ladder and joined the boys. There was a wonderful view across the fields to the hills. I could see them in the middle distance, in a fine, sunny mist dotted with trees. The little house was below us, surrounded by the tall trees. Already the willows had a bright yellow green colour to them, shining in the sun. Soon they would be covered in leaves again. The bright February sun shone through the open cottage windows, and on the red mossy tiles of the old roof where the sparrows had started noisily making nests again. I had seen them busily flying about with pieces of straw in their beaks and odd lumps of wool that they had found caught on the hedges and gate. The baby birds at Monk's Green would all have lovely soft nests this year.

There was a cold start to March, with a bright ice-blue sky dotted with small puffs of cloud, and a chill breeze ruffling the long, purple catkins at the tops of the poplars. Two magpies had started visiting the chicken run in the early mornings, and I was often woken shortly before six o'clock by their noisy chattering as they bobbed about the hen trough.

They were large, handsome birds, but I had to admit to a certain dislike for them. There are many superstitions concerning magpies and they are generally thought to be birds of ill omen, probably due to their habit of robbing the nests of other birds and eating their eggs and fledglings. I was always slightly wary of looking out of the window at them, and would wait to make sure from their chatterings that they were both there. Irrational as it seemed, I felt that if there was only one magpie there the day would go badly, whereas two would bring good luck, as in the old rhyme:

> One for sorrow, two for joy,
> Three a girl and four a boy;
> Five is a wish and six a kiss,
> Seven for a letter and eight for something better.

There were more sinister versions with,

> Four as death, five for heaven and six for hell,
> And seven the devil himself.

Gerald always laughed at my superstitions. However, he had not quite forgotten the time several years earlier when he had insisted on picking a bunch of snowdrops to take to work with him and put on his desk.

'You shouldn't take snowdrops inside,' I had said, 'it's unlucky.'

'That's nonsense,' he had replied.

However, at lunch-time he had walked around the town to do some shopping, slipped and broken his ankle and had it in plaster for the next seven weeks. He stated firmly that the pavements were icy, as could be expected in February, and it was pure coincidence. But I never saw him pick snowdrops again.

The magpies were usually lucky and found some food left from the hens' previous evening feed. They always made a great deal of noise over their meal, bobbing their long blue-black tails up and down as they perched, in a somewhat ungainly fashion, on the edge of the trough. One of them then usually flew up onto the top of the hen house, calling 'clak, clak' across to the wood. Sometimes there were answering calls from the far trees, sometimes there was silence.

They would both fly to the old, twisted apple tree and hop about in the lichened branches. Then they were gone—over the lane and across the field in front of the cottage to the farm, where I had seen their large, twiggy nest in the top of a thorn tree.

We went to a concert on Sunday evening in Wetherbury church—the beautiful church of cool, grey stone with a wonderful timbered roof. It had been a warm, still day, one of those perfect spring days when the air smells of summer, and the evening air still has some warmth in it.

The church was cool inside as we stepped through the open doorway onto the smooth, tiled floor. We sat and waited, while the church filled with people. Gerald was studying the programme, but Katy and Tom were watching the musicians coming into the church through a low, narrow door at one side, with their black cases of assorted sizes holding violins, cellos and flutes. I turned and looked at them, too, all very smart in their dark clothes and shining black patent shoes. The girls in the orchestra were wearing long black velvet skirts and white blouses covered with frills. The players began undoing their cases and laughing with each other as they tuned their instruments.

I was surprised how young most of them looked, not much older than Katy—young, pretty girls, fair-haired boys. They were all smiling, talking quietly to each other without any sign of animosity, but I wondered at the secret fears and hates and jealousies of them all; so many lives bound up so closely with each other, so many individuals striving when they played to produce one glorious volume of music.

The musicians took their places and then the concert began—Vivaldi's 'Four Seasons', my favourite piece of music, the music that I had been listening to that day when Gerald had returned from London and first seen our little Tudor house in the fields. I thought of that day and all that had happened in between, the tears and the laughter. I looked at Gerald, but his face was expressionless, looking straight ahead, and I had no idea what he was thinking.

'Four Seasons'. I'd had my sheep for four seasons now, spring, summer, autumn and winter, and now it was back to spring again, the cold of winter left behind, the warmth and sunlight of summer ahead.

The music of summer began quietly with a gentle violin solo drifting up to the rafters, and then the music quickened

150

pace. The programme called this 'The Shepherd's Lament', and I thought of Ian. How perverse life was. When Ian had lived three miles away I had seen him seldom and rarely thought of him, but now that he was five hundred miles away, I found myself thinking of him often. I pictured him walking over the hills with his crook and his sheepdog, and wished that I was there, too, walking beside him.

The music flowed on. I would have wished it to last for ever. But then it was over. The clapping rose to a crescendo and the audience began to get up from their seats and file out, chattering, smiling, their shoes tapping, clicking and scraping over the old tiles.

We drifted out into the churchyard and I lingered in the warm air under the yew trees as Gerald and the children walked towards the car. I wanted to go to the blue hills and walk over them in the moonlight; I wanted to go to Scotland and be with Ian: I wanted the music to go on forever.

We drove home, through the darkened town, through the quiet, ancient villages of timbered houses, home to our little cottage in the fields.

'Wasn't it wonderful?' I said. 'It always sounds so good in a church. It's the perfect place for a concert. The music echoes round the walls and up to the high roof. It really was wonderful.' I sighed. 'But it always ends so quickly. It never seems to go on long enough.'

'Yes, I enjoyed it, too,' said Gerald. 'You have the record, of course, but it never seems the same as actually watching people playing.'

We arrived home and the children, after a mug of cocoa and some chocolate biscuits, were soon in bed.

'I'm going to sit in the garden for a while,' I said, 'it's such a lovely evening.'

'Would you like a drink?' asked Gerald. 'What do you want—whisky, or shall we have some wine?'

'Let's have some wine, shall we? Let's open a bottle of Rodney's blackberry wine.'

I went out into the garden and across to the barn. I could smell the sweet smell of hay and hear the steady chomping

151

of Pandora's and Berkeley's jaws. I did not put their light on, but said goodnight softly to them. They replied with muffled bleats, their mouths full.

I went back to the bench under the kitchen window and Gerald came out with two glasses of wine, the bottle wedged precariously under his arm. We sat on the bench in the warm night air, sipping our wine, and I watched the cluster of moths round the outside light over the back door. The cats appeared through the hedge and began chasing about over the lawn, after moths, after each other.

We sat there until quite late, while the moon made long shadows of the poplars over the field. As I drank the rich, red wine, I thought of Rodney and wondered what he was doing so far away, and whether I should ever see him again.

The following evening Katy was sitting at the kitchen table struggling with her homework as usual—the hated geography this time—and Gerald and I were watching the television news in the sitting-room with Tom, who had had his bath and was sitting in his dressing-gown with me on the sofa. The news always seemed more or less the same to me—the disasters went on, only the places changed. Gerald always watched the news every evening if he was in, but I was now much more interested in the weather report. Would my beasts have a fine day tomorrow? Would a prolonged drought wither up all their food?

I heard the telephone ring and then Katy put her head round the door:

'It's for you, Mother.'

I followed her, shutting the door behind me, and picked up the phone. There was a man's voice on the other end. It was David Roberts.

'Elizabeth? Do you still want a bottle lamb? I've got a little pure-bred Ryeland you can have if you do.'

'David, hello. I'd love one, I really would. How old is it? Is it a ewe or a ram?'

'It's a week old. It was a ram, but I've put a ring on it. It's a bit of a runt and will never be any good for breeding, but if you want one just as a pet he'll be ideal.'

'Oh, he sounds wonderful. What happened to his mother? Did she die?'

'No, she's got mastitis, so she can't feed him. I wondered if you'd like to come over tomorrow and fetch him, and I could show you round the farm and the other sheep, if you're interested.'

'That sounds a lovely idea—let me just get a pencil and you can tell me how to get there.'

Tom appeared as I was scribbling directions all over the top of yesterday's *Guardian*, and after I had put the phone down he said in a loud voice:

'Who was that? Are you getting another lamb?'

'Shush,' I said, looking towards the closed sitting-room door, 'it's going to be a surprise.'

'What is it?' asked Katy. 'Another one like Pandora?'

'No, its a little white Ryeland. Remember we saw some at the autumn show at Peterborough? It's a ram, well, a wether,' I added.

'Will it be here when we get back from school?' asked Tom.

Gerald appeared from the sitting-room.

'Come on, young man, up to bed,' he said to Tom.

'What was the weather report?' I asked. 'Is it going to stay fine?'

'Lovely wether tomorrow, Mother,' said Tom, grinning wickedly as he ran upstairs.